*"The level of engagement by any person*

*in the life and ministry of a local*

*congregation is largely determined*

*by the level of relational*

*connections they experience."*

**Dr. Phil Maynard**

# Shift 2.0

ACTIVATION

GUIDE

## by Dr. Phil Maynard

Market
Square
BOOKS

# Shift 2.0
## *Activation Guide*

### by Dr. Phil Maynard

©2018 Phil Maynard
books@marketsquarebooks.com
P.O. Box 23664  Knoxville, Tennessee 37933


ISBN: 978-1-7323092-3-4


Library of Congress: 2018961926


Printed and Bound in the United States of America


Editors: Kristin Lighter and Kevin Slimp
Cover Illustration ©2018 Market Square Publishing, LLC

# Table of Contents

# Welcome!

The chances are good that you have already discovered what a valuable resource *Shift 2.0* is for helping congregations discover more effective ways to do ministry in a rapidly changing culture. Churches all over the country are using the 5 shifts to frame a conversation about the health of their ministries in the context of their local cultural shifts. This is exciting!

The *Shift 2.0 Activation Guide* is designed specifically to support pastors and church leadership teams as they consider the shifts recommended and how they might be accomplished in their setting. You will find the 5 shifts broken down into sections framed around **Guiding Principles**. These **Guiding Principles** are the big picture things that connect the best practices to the goal of effective ministry.

Throughout the *Activation Guide, after each* **Guiding Principle,** you will find a template for developing SMART goals and action plans. It is my recommendation that for each shift your team develops two goals/action plans.

The first goal is focused on what can be done to improve the effectiveness of this theme (e.g. Hospitality, Worship, Discipleship etc.) within the local church.

The second goal is focused on what can be done to connect this theme to the surrounding community. For example, a congregation might develop a hospitality center to create a sense of welcome and encourage the development of relationships between people already at the church. That same congregation might also develop a goal to build connections through a variety of social media tools with the surrounding community. One of these goals is focused inside the church. One of these goals is focused outside the church. There is a SMART goal and action plan template after every **Guiding Principle**, as noted above, but it is highly unlikely (and not even advisable) that you will develop a SMART goal and action plan for each principle. They are included after each section for convenience sake, but you should focus on the areas that seem the greatest priority or the most sensible place to start for your church – you can't do everything at once – think about what changes will have the greatest impact for your setting. As you begin to accomplish your goals, move forward with new ones.

I suggest (following the recommendation of Simon Sinek's *Start With Why*) that the team begin with the question "Why?" It's hard to get motivated to do anything differently if we can't see the reason for the change.

For example, in working with congregations all around the country, I have never had a leadership team say, "We are not a friendly church." The reality is that every church considers itself to be friendly. It is not until we take a deeper look at practices that actually communicate that we are friendly that we discover we are really not very friendly.

The survey tool provided at the beginning of each section is a good way to start the conversation.

Each section includes a variety of brief assessments and reflections to assist the leadership team in evaluating the effectiveness of particular dimensions of ministry and what might be helpful to move the congregation forward. These are labelled as **Team Activities**, and you will benefit greatly if you complete them. They can also be used as reflective exercises for individuals if you are not in a group setting.

It is my prayer that you will find this resource helpful, that you will discover more about your church, and that you will be blessed with amazing effectiveness in accomplishing God's plan for engaging your community.


Dr. Phil Maynard
Director, Excellence in Ministry Coaching (EMC3)

# Shift 1

## From Fellowship to Hospitality

"My command is this: Love each other
as I have loved you."

**—Jesus, John 15:12 (NIV)**

Life is not about stuff we own or accumulate. It is not even about
personal accomplishment. Life is about people. We can replace
stuff, but we can't replace people!

**—Michael Slaughter, Momentum for Life (1)**

As a school for love, the church becomes a congregation where
people learn from one another how to love.

**—Bishop Robert Schnase, Five Practices of Fruitful Congregations (2)**

# Congregational Survey

A survey to be completed by leadership and congregation members to evaluate the quality of hospitality within your church. After reading the statement to the left, rate your response from 1-4 with 4 representing strong agreement and 1 representing disagreement.

*(1 = Poor....4= Amazing)*

| | **From Fellowship to Hospitality** | 1 | 2 | 3 | 4 |
|---|---|---|---|---|---|
| 1. | Visitors are engaged in conversation by a participant in worship seeking to learn about them and their needs. | | | | |
| 2. | Most members have a close friend or group of friends who are regular participants in the worship and discipleship activities of this congregation. | | | | |
| 3. | This congregation attracts people from a variety of cultural groups and provides a place where all feel welcome. | | | | |
| 4. | This congregation is actively involved in the life of the immediately surrounding community, making a difference and friends in the process. | | | | |
| 5. | Following worship, the church provides an easily visible space with refreshments and encourages participants to invite someone new to join them for fellowship. | | | | |
| 6. | The people in this congregation put relationships above whatever issues might be divisive. | | | | |

| | | 1 | 2 | 3 | 4 |
|---|---|---|---|---|---|
| 7. | Worship leadership provides training and actively encourages participants to engage those who may be new or unknown. | | | | |
| 8. | When someone misses worship for more than two consecutive weekends, there is someone who makes contact. | | | | |
| 9. | Following the first visit to our worship, the person/family receives a brief visit and a welcome gift from a lay person. | | | | |
| 10. | When someone has been in worship three or more weeks, they are invited into a relationship with a sponsor/guide to help them get connected in a meaningful way. | | | | |
| 11. | Following the second visit, a newcomer is invited to participate in a 'get to know you' interview with the pastor. | | | | |
| 12. | By not asking people to introduce themselves, our congregation avoids putting people on the spot during the worship welcome time. | | | | |
| 13. | Our facilities are clean and free of clutter for weekly worship experiences. | | | | |
| 14. | We offer some form of informational meeting at the conclusion of worship for those who would like to know more about the ministry of the congregation. | | | | |
| 15. | Our congregation offers a first class nursery during worship with trained staff, bright and clean facilities, sanitized toys, and a parent notification system. | | | | |
| 16. | Our church website is attractive, full of stories, up-to-date, and provides easy access to pertinent information about worship (including directions). | | | | |

|     |     | 1 | 2 | 3 | 4 |
|-----|-----|---|---|---|---|
| 17. | This church offers a variety of attractional events and programs to introduce people in the community to our ministries. | | | | |
| 18. | We encourage our leaders and members to actively engage in networking with friends, neighbors, relatives, and associates to build relationships and introduce them to Jesus. | | | | |
| 19. | We actively support the invitational process by providing attractive, professional quality invitations to special events, sermon series, and seasonal emphases. | | | | |
| 20. | Our congregation is actively engaged in the life of the community, building relationships and sharing the love of Christ. | | | | |
| 21. | We have a system for engaging worship participants, particularly newcomers, in small groups or other discipleship partnering relationships. | | | | |
| 22. | We train our members and regular attenders in the basics of conflict management. | | | | |
| 23. | There is a system in place for providing pastoral care for our members that includes lay participation and leadership. | | | | |
| 24. | Our communication tools (bulletins, flyers, newsletters, postcards, etc.) are of professional quality and avoid insider language. | | | | |
| 25. | We encourage and celebrate the development of relationships beyond the congregation, making this a priority over attending church activities. | | | | |

A perfect score on this survey would be 100 points.

When using this with your leadership team or congregation, here is how you determine an average score: Total the points for each individual survey. Add the points from all the individual surveys together. Divide that total number by the number of surveys that were completed. This gives you an average score (out of 100 possible points), providing you with a "grade" for your congregational health in this area. Using a standard academic scale:

| | | |
|---|---|---|
| 90+ | = | A |
| 80-89 | = | B |
| 70-79 | = | C |
| 60-69 | = | D |

What grade does your hospitality receive? What did the survey reveal? What is your strongest area? What do you hope for in hospitality? Write your answers in the space below:

# INTERPERSONAL HOSPITALITY

**Refers to the level and quality of relational connections within the congregation, the people we know.**

# Guiding Principle

**The level of engagement by any person in the life and ministry of a local congregation is largely determined by the level of relational connections they experience.**

There are several very practical considerations when it comes to living in authentic relationship with each other as disciples of Jesus Christ. The *Shift 2.0* book presents three keys to authentic relationships: forgiveness, acceptance, and accountability (pp. 18-19).

The following practical explorations of these ideas will help you consider how these themes are lived out in your congregation.

## Forgiveness

The reality is that there will always be disagreements about things when you get more than one person together. We all bring our perspectives and opinions. The issue is not that we disagree. It is how we deal with things when we disagree.

The biblical model for dealing with conflict in the church is found in Matthew, chapter 18. The following is a summary:

- **Level 1:** Go, in private, to reconcile with the person...if this doesn't work
- **Level 2:** Go with a mediator seeking to reconcile...if this doesn't work
- **Level 3:** Take it to the church (leadership) to work out.

What kind of procedure has your congregation developed to deal with conflict?

## Acceptance

The big question here is how does the church relate to and welcome those who are different than you?

# TEAM ACTIVITY!

Jesus seemed to purposefully hang out with people who were not like him. They seemed drawn to his company. How well does your church do this? One way to get clarity on this is to take a look at the demographics in your community and compare them to the demographics of your congregation. Using your Mission-Insite Report (explained in detail in the *Shift 2.0* book), complete the following survey of community demographics:

**EXPLORING WHO IS IN OUR COMMUNITY THROUGH DEMOGRAPHICS**

**Using the Demographic Report provided, describe the community your congregation is called to serve using demographic facts.**

POPULATION TRENDS:

What is the population of your study area? _____

Is the population projected to grow or decline? _____

By what percentage? _____

By how many households? _____

AGE TRENDS:

What is the average age in the community? _____

Is the area growing older or younger? _____

INCOME TRENDS:

What is the average household income? _____

Is the average income growing or declining? _____

GENERATIONAL TRENDS:

Which group has the largest presence in the area? _____

Which grouphas the smallest presence? _____

Which group has the greatest growth projectsd?_____

Which group has the greatest decline projected? _____

RACIAL/ETHNIC TRENDS:

What is the percentage represented by each racial/ethnic group?

_____

Which group has the highest projected growth? _____

Which groupd is projected to have the greatest decline? _____

How do the demographics of the community match up with the demographics of your congregation?

What does that tell you about the level of acceptance that is felt by the various demographic groups?

## Accountability

A central theme in the admonitions of the Apostle Paul called the 'one anothers' is that of accountability. For example: submit to one another, encourage one another, admonish one another, bear with one another, agree with one another, and live in harmony with one another.

This is also the foundation for the Wesleyan understanding of Christian Discipleship in the model (developed by Methodism's founder, John Wesley).

There are several ways to help build in accountability for the local congregation:

- Make small group ministries a centerpiece of congregational life. This creates a shift from anonymity (sitting in the pews) to accountability where strong friendships are established and we are invited to engage our faith journey more fully.

- Teach the 'one anothers'.
- Train the congregation in appropriate ways to deal with conflict.
- Provide training in caring for one another.

One of the most helpful tools in developing a culture of accountability, particularly in the way we engage one another, is a by developing a shared Behavioral Covenant.

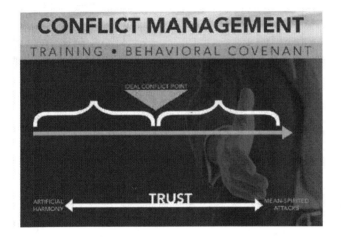

### BEHAVIORAL COVENANT

- A written document
- Drawn up and owned by the congregation
- Describing positively how they wish to be treated and will treat one another
- A spiritual discipline practiced regularly

It is recommended that at least the leadership team in every congregation develop a Behavioral Covenant. Many congregations have found this to be helpful congregation-wide. A free PowerPoint presentation about building a Behavioral Covenant is available at emc3coaching.com.

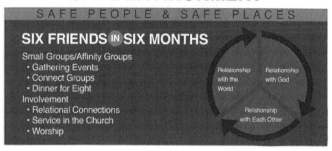

**INTERPERSONAL HOSPITALITY:**

Refers to the level of quality of relational connections within the congregation - the people we know.

## CREATING A
## SAFE ENVIRONMENT

SAFE PEOPLE & SAFE PLACES

### SIX FRIENDS IN SIX MONTHS

Small Groups/Affinity Groups
- Gathering Events
- Connect Groups
- Dinner for Eight

Involvement
- Relational Connections
- Service in the Church
- Worship

Relationship with the World
Relationship with God
Relationship with Each Other

As noted in the previous image, one of the keys to developing interpersonal hospitality is to help people develop friendships within the congregation.

Statistically, research shows that unless a newcomer to the congregation *develops six friends in their first six months*, there is a high probability that they will go somewhere else to try and find those relationships.

The following are some ways that are recommended to help people begin making those relational connections:

- Provide a hospitality center with refreshments that serves as a gathering place and is especially focused on engaging newcomers in conversation.

- Host gathering events with opportunities for people to be at table groups and engage in conversation.

- Provide Connect Groups (groups formed around the needs and interests of participants):
  - Biking

  - Quilting

  - Sewing

- ○ Bowling
- ○ Fishing
- ○ Golfing.
- The opportunities are as varied as the interests of people in the congregation!
- Provide a variety of short-term studies around topics of interest.
- Provide service opportunities focused on meeting needs in the community
- Form a 'Dinner for Eight' program to encourage table fellowship and building of relationships.
- Help people learn how to share their stories.

## Questions for conversation around Interpersonal hospitality:

- How are relationships encouraged and supported by your congregation?

- What is the system for engaging participants in small group gatherings (like Connect groups or affinity groups)?

- How do members of this congregation care for one another?

Build a SMART goal and action plan to advance the practices of Interpersonal Hospitality using the template provided.

## SMART GOAL WITH "SO THAT " STATEMENT

Ministry: _____    Date: _____

| List Goal statement below: |
|---|
|  |

WRITE ONE STATEMENT PER PAGE WITH ACTION PLANS BELOW

| WHAT ARE WE DOING? | WHO WILL DO IT? (NAME) | BY WHEN WILL WE COMPLETE THIS TASK? MM/DD/YY | RESOURCES NEEDED | ADDITIONAL COMMENTS |
|---|---|---|---|---|
|  |  |  |  |  |
|  |  |  |  |  |
|  |  |  |  |  |
|  |  |  |  |  |
|  |  |  |  |  |
|  |  |  |  |  |
|  |  |  |  |  |
|  |  |  |  |  |
|  |  |  |  |  |
|  |  |  |  |  |
|  |  |  |  |  |
|  |  |  |  |  |
|  |  |  |  |  |
|  |  |  |  |  |

USE ADDITIONAL PAGES AS NEEDED TO CLEARLY COMMUNICATE
YOUR TASK TO ACCOMPLISH THE GOAL

# INTENTIONAL HOSPITALITY

**Refers to the practices of members and the congregation in making relational connections with people they don't know who are visiting and/or returning.**

# Guiding Principle

**People who visit a church return and/or stay connected because they are engaged as friends and feel like they could fit into this congregation.**

## Platform Experiences

This refers to the basic practices of hospitality that are expected by guests as they connect with your congregation for the first time:

- Parking lot greeters
- Entryway greeters (at all entry points)
- Ushers
- Congregational greeting
- Connect cards/pew pads to get pertinent information
- Information packets
- Follow-up letter and/or phone call
- Clean and uncluttered facilities.

Take a moment and circle the 'platform experiences' your congregation has in place and provides consistently.

How did you do?

Remember, these are what people expect you to do. If you do them, you don't get any extra points. If you don't do them, people may think you don't really care about guests.

# TEAM ACTIVITY!

On the following page is a facilities assessment. Take a tour of your current ministry facility with your team, then complete the assessment (either as a group, reaching a group consensus on each rating, or as individuals, after which you compare your individual ratings).

## Assessing our Facilities

**Using the following chart, rate the condition and adequacy of the church facilities. (1=poor and 5=excellent)**

| | 1 | 2 | 3 | 4 | 5 |
|---|---|---|---|---|---|
| Lawn/ Landscaping | 1 | 2 | 3 | 4 | 5 |
| Sidewalks – clean & edged | 1 | 2 | 3 | 4 | 5 |
| Nursery – clean, bright colors, well stocked | 1 | 2 | 3 | 4 | 5 |
| Adequate classroom space | 1 | 2 | 3 | 4 | 5 |
| Adequate parking | 1 | 2 | 3 | 4 | 5 |
| Designated visitor & handicap parking | 1 | 2 | 3 | 4 | 5 |
| Clearly identified entry to worship space | 1 | 2 | 3 | 4 | 5 |
| No negative signage – "keep out," "no food." | 1 | 2 | 3 | 4 | 5 |
| Adequate room signs | 1 | 2 | 3 | 4 | 5 |
| Hallways – free of items and bright | 1 | 2 | 3 | 4 | 5 |
| Walls – clean & free of damage | 1 | 2 | 3 | 4 | 5 |
| Carpets – clean & in good repair | 1 | 2 | 3 | 4 | 5 |
| Bathrooms – clean, brightly lit, stocked | 1 | 2 | 3 | 4 | 5 |
| Tile floors – clean & waxed | 1 | 2 | 3 | 4 | 5 |
| Worship space – not cluttered | 1 | 2 | 3 | 4 | 5 |
| Handicapped accessible | 1 | 2 | 3 | 4 | 5 |

If the goal is to make people feel really welcome and to leave with a sense that they could belong with your congregation, simply providing the 'platform level' experiences is not sufficient.

In the *Shift 2.0* book, Phil describes a scenario (a real life example) of visiting with a local congregation on the east coast of Florida. Take a moment to read this account again (aloud, if you are with a group). What did you notice that was different from the platform level experiences described previously?

## Platform Level Experiences

- Parking Lot Greeters
- Entryway Greeters
- Ushers
- Congregational Greeting
- Connect Cards
- Information Packet
- Follow-up Letter/Phone Call

## *Beyond* Platform Level Experiences

### HELPFUL HITS

- Reserve the best parking for first-time guests
- Station greeters outside the building
- Have music playing when people enter the worship space
- Allow guests to remain anonymous
- Offer a warm public welcome
- Offer refreshments at each service

### HOSPITALITY CENTER

- Space for connections
- Refreshments
- Directions/Information

### INFORMATIONAL MEETING

- Who we are
- What we believe
- How we serve

Several suggestions are made in the Intentional Hospitality portion of this section of *Shift 2.0* about moving beyond platform level experiences:

- We cannot overemphasize the importance of a hospitality center where refreshments are available before and after worship. This is a place that is staffed by your volunteers with the best hospitality skills. It is the location that guests are invited to following worship to begin making connections. The type of refreshments is not as important as the intentional conversations between staff, members, and guests.

- Many congregations provide welcome gifts. Some congregations make them available at the hospitality center and others deliver them through a porch visit.

- Connect cards are utilized to secure contact information from both members and guests.

- A connecting interview is scheduled following the 2nd visit of a guest. This can be done by the pastor, a hospitality team member, or a staff member. The interview is usually held at a local restaurant or coffee shop. The focus is getting to know the guest. This is not a time for selling the programs of the church. Phil will tell you that this is the most significant thing impacting the consistent growth in his congregations.

- A follow-up letter is provided (using the "Producer" model template offered in the *Shift 2.0* book).

- Multiple means of contact are utilized over a period of 5-6 weeks from the initial visit.

- Guests are engaged in conversation by regular attenders of the congregation, not just the pastor.

- An attractive and safe nursery is provided (a must for young families).

- The congregation is trained to welcome and engage in conversation those they do not know (see suggestions in *Shift 2.0* book).

- Informational meetings are held so that guests can learn about what the church believes and how the church is involved in the community.

- All communications are done with excellence.

- Negative signage is removed from the property.

As you ponder this list of 'beyond platform level' experiences, what catches your attention?  What could your congregation do to increase the level of Intentional Hospitality?

Build a SMART goal and action plan to advance the practices of Intentional Hospitality using the template provided.

## SMART GOAL WITH "SO THAT " STATEMENT

Ministry: _____ Date: _____

List Goal statement below:

WRITE ONE STATEMENT PER PAGE WITH ACTION PLANS BELOW

| WHAT ARE WE DOING? | WHO WILL DO IT? (NAME) | BY WHEN WILL WE COMPLETE THIS TASK? MM/DD/YY | RESOURCES NEEDED | ADDITIONAL COMMENTS |
|---|---|---|---|---|
| | | | | |
| | | | | |
| | | | | |
| | | | | |
| | | | | |
| | | | | |
| | | | | |
| | | | | |
| | | | | |
| | | | | |
| | | | | |
| | | | | |
| | | | | |

USE ADDITIONAL PAGES AS NEEDED TO CLEARLY COMMUNICATE
YOUR TASK TO ACCOMPLISH THE GOAL

# INVITATIONAL HOSPITALITY

**Refers to the connections made by the congregation with people they don't know who are out in the community.**

# Guiding Principle

**The vast majority of people who visit a church come because someone invited them. People discover God's love in and through a relationship with a disciple of Jesus Christ.**

Consider the following statements:

*Statistically, somewhere between 60-80% of people who come to the church come because they are invited by a friend. (3)*

*According to Bishop Bob Farr, in **Get Their Name**, the average United Methodist invites someone to church once every 38 years. (4)*

The truth is hard to miss. If we don't invite people to church, the majority of them won't come, and they will miss out on the blessing of a relationship with Jesus. And we will miss out on fulfilling our mission to *"Make disciples of Jesus Christ for the transformation of the world."*

Phil suggests two tracks for living into Invitational Hospitality. Let's start with the personal track. Jim Ozier, in ***Clip In*** (5), suggests that part of the problem we experience in helping people live into this calling is that they have to work up to the actual inviting. He uses the graphic below to illustrate a more natural progression:

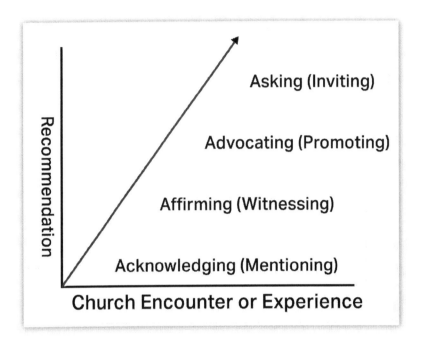

How might your congregational leadership help people from the congregation move through this progression?

The second track is the connection-building support of the local church:

- **Personal Connections:** Business cards provided to members that include the times of worship and directions to the church (they write their own name on the card).

- **Postcards and/or flyers:** Graphically designed tools used to promote things like a new sermon series or a seasonal focus. They are provided for regular attenders to use when inviting someone to come.

- **The Joe Harding method** (described in *Shift 2.0*): Used during worship to encourage invitations.

- **Networking:** The building of relationships by the pastor and key lay leadership with those in leadership/business roles in the community.

- **Attractional ministries:** Activities hosted at the church inviting community participation. Often included are things like fall festivals, Trunk R Treat, Vacation Bible School, a pumpkin patch, block parties, and concerts.

- **Servant Evangelism:** A model of reaching into the community through service projects. A great resource for this is an article by Steve Sjogren of the Vineyard Church – "94 Community Servant Evangelism Ideas for Your Church" (which you can find easily by typing the article name into your favorite search engine).

- **Marketing:** Thinking beyond traditional marketing techniques (phone solicitation, direct mail, telephone book and newspaper advertisements that have limited impact and tend to be expensive. The website is your most important tool with over 90% of people checking out the website before visiting a church. The following page includes an assessment tool for your website.

- **Social Media:** Encouraging regular attenders to post about the activities of the church or tweet about a message (a great way to reach out into the community).

# TEAM ACTIVITY!

Use the chart below to evaluate how you are doing with your current social media offerings.

| Criteria | Assessment | Notes |
|---|---|---|
| Professional looking site | | |
| Website is kept current | | |
| Worship times clearly identified/worship style described | | |
| Clear directions to the church | | |
| Information about childcare | | |
| Information about staff | | |
| Current messages from worship are available | | |
| Stories about lives changed or community impact | | |
| Pictures of the congregation at worship, play, service | | |

Which of these suggestions seems to be a helpful leverage point for your congregation in continuing to develop the level of Invitational Hospitality?

Build a SMART goal and action plan to advance the practices of Invitational Hospitality using the template provided.

## SMART GOAL WITH "SO THAT " STATEMENT

Ministry: _____   Date: _____

List Goal statement below:

WRITE ONE STATEMENT PER PAGE WITH ACTION PLANS BELOW

| WHAT ARE WE DOING? | WHO WILL DO IT? (NAME) | BY WHEN WILL WE COMPLETE THIS TASK? MM/DD/YY | RESOURCES NEEDED | ADDITIONAL COMMENTS |
|---|---|---|---|---|
| | | | | |
| | | | | |
| | | | | |
| | | | | |
| | | | | |
| | | | | |
| | | | | |
| | | | | |
| | | | | |
| | | | | |
| | | | | |
| | | | | |
| | | | | |

USE ADDITIONAL PAGES AS NEEDED TO CLEARLY COMMUNICATE
YOUR TASK TO ACCOMPLISH THE GOAL

# INCARNATIONAL HOSPITALITY

**Refers to the personal engagement by regular participants in the congregation in building relationships with those we know outside the church in order to be Christ to the unchurched.**

# Guiding Principle

**People come to a relationship with Jesus through a relationship with disciples who serve as the presence of Christ in their lives.**

Let's be clear:

- The mission of the church is to make disciples of Jesus Christ.

- Most people come to a relationship with Jesus through a relationship with a disciple of Jesus.

- It is the relationship that provides the level of trust that allows us the opportunity to invite people to discover Jesus.

It is the calling of every disciple to build those kinds of relationships and to invite people into a relationship with Jesus.

So . . . how does the church support the building of those relationships?

## Relationships start with Conversations

This may surprise you, but many people express a feeling of discomfort when asked to talk with someone they don't know. In a world of posts and tweets and hundreds of 'friends' that we don't even know, the church has an opportunity to model a different kind of community. And it starts with a conversation.

The following framework is a tool for helping people make meaningful connections and build relationships that matter:

# How We Create Relationships

The Excellence in Ministry Coaching team has worked with a surprising number of churches that have expressed a need to help their members and friends learn how to build relationships. This is, of course, a foundational practice in the church since ...

- First-time guests are much more likely to feel welcome if worship participants engage them in conversation and begin to build a relationship.

- Making disciples most often begins with a conversation leading to a relationship and then leading to a decision to begin the journey of discipleship.

- Members becoming engaged in the life and ministry of the congregation begin this connection through conversations, the building of strong relationships, and developing friendships.

- Those persons engaged through service by the congregation are much more likely to discover the love of Jesus as the people serving enter into conversations and develop relationships.

This practice of having conversations and building relationships is a big deal!

How do we really create a relationship? We expedite this process by building a framework to help congregations make meaningful connections and build relationships that matter.

- First, we must catch each other's attention. This may take the form of mentioning a family's children or appreciating a person's attire, using the proximity of location as an inroad to begin a conversation, or just mentioning that you don't know them even though they are sitting next to you and inviting a conversation.

- Once we have gotten each other's attention, we need to establish an interest in having a conversation. The obvious interest for those already worshiping together would be their tenure at the church or involvement in church activities or, in the case of first time guests, their experience or how they came to try this church. This movement of establishing an interest could include conversation around families, schools, sports, hobbies, or even favorite restaurants.

- There usually follows a period of exploration - of asking and answering each other's questions, of probing for areas of common interest, of testing whether the other has anything to contribute to us, and whether we have anything to contribute to the other. The key here is learning to ask good questions. Be curious!

One way we explore our identities is "our story." We grow up, we encounter challenges, large and small, and we figure out what to do. And the way we figure it out at these choice points reveals the value and interests that really count with us. So, one of the most direct forms of exploration is to learn each other's stories and focusing on choice points. Why did you go to school here rather than there? Why did you study this rather than that? Why did you decide to emigrate rather than remain at home? As we begin learning each other's answers to these questions, we learn more about each other, what moves us, and what we have to contribute.

- As a result of our exploration, we may begin to make exchanges - not just in the future, but then and there within the conversation. We may turn out to be a good listener for someone who needs listening. We may find we are learning a great deal from our interaction with the other person. We may find we have an opportunity to offer another person some insight, support, or recognition that they find valuable.

We may find we can challenge the other person in ways that may bring them new insight. We may also discover a basis for future "exchanges" – such as going to see a movie we both want to see, deciding to come to an event or activity the other has told us about, or just deciding to have another conversation.

• Finally, if we've determined a basis may exist for a relationship, we make a commitment to the relationship by agreeing to meet again, have coffee, come to the meeting, send emails, etc. What turns the exchange into a relationship is the commitment we make to each other and to the relationship. People often make the mistake of trying to go right to a commitment without laying a relational basis for it first.

Want to know more about how to help your congregation develop relationships that matter? A much fuller treatment is provided in Phil's book, Connect! Creating a Culture of Relationships That Matter. How might you use this (or a similar resource) to help your congregation learn how to develop relationships?

## Encourage Neighborliness

Perhaps Jesus really meant it when he summarized the teachings of the law into two major themes:

- Love God (with all your mind, all your heart, all your soul, and all your strength)
- Love Your Neighbor.

The neighborhoods in which our regular attenders live are our greatest and potentially most receptive mission field:

- In every community the percentage of people NOT involved in any type of faith community ranges from 60-80%. You can see the specifics for your community in the Quad Report from MissionInsite. (3)

- Our best opportunity to be the presence of Christ in people's lives is in our own neighborhoods with people that we know and who know us.

- As Lovett Weems (acclaimed author and church/leadership consultant) puts it: *"we have to earn the right to be heard."* (4) We live in a culture that needs to be convinced of the love of Jesus for them.

Here are some practical ideas for being good neighbors:

- Help someone during a difficult time.

  ○ Provide transportation to and from the doctor during a health crisis.

  ○ Provide childcare when someone has to be away for some unexpected need.

  ○ Provide meals for a family dealing with hospitalization or loss.

  ○ Share movies with someone who is recuperating.

- Welcome newcomers to the neighborhood.

  ○ Take a welcome gift – cookies, pie, or cake and some drinks.

  ○ Offer to help unpack boxes.

  ○ Invite them over for dinner since their kitchen is not set up yet.

  ○ Share insights into trusted mechanics, doctors, restaurants, etc.

- Provide neighborhood gatherings.
  ○ Have a cookout in your yard.

  ○ Set up a play date for the kids.

  ○ Host an outdoor movie night.

  ○ Start a book club.

  ○ Invite neighbors over for a game night.

  ○ Start a walking group.

- Adopt a lonely person.

  ○ Invite neighbors without family nearby to holiday gatherings.

  ○ Have neighbors over for a game or movie night.

- Offer a house watching service.

  ◦ Offer to keep an eye on properties while neighbors are away.

  ◦ Establish a neighborhood watch.

  ◦ Collect mail while neighbors are away.

  ◦ Feed and walk dogs while neighbors are away.

- Create a neighborhood map and contact list:

  ◦ Draw the neighborhood and identify the family for each home.

  ◦ Provide contact information for each home.

Of course the list could be much longer.

How can you encourage members to begin connecting with their neighbors?

How can the church help facilitate neighborhood gatherings?

- Provide resources for gatherings: grills, paper goods, cooking utensils, charcoal/gas.
- Hold Vacation Bible School in a neighborhood instead of the church.
- Encourage small group gatherings in homes rather than the church, making it easier to invite neighbors.

# TEAM ACTIVITY!

**Love Your Neighbor Exercise:** Try this with your team and perhaps even with your congregation. Identify the 5 families living in closest proximity to you and write down responses to each of the items of knowledge about that neighbor. When you are done calculate the number of points earned using the point distribution for each item.

How did you do?

What might it mean for developing relationships and being the presence of Christ if we were to have this level of connection with our neighbors?

## Love Your Neighbor Exercise

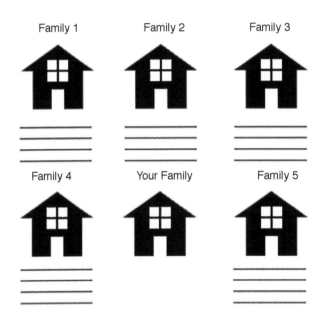

- Can you address all family members by name?
- Do you know what the career(s) are of the parent(s)?
- Have you been in each others homes? Had a real conversation?
- Have you shared a meal with that family?

How many of the families were you able to respond 'yes' to all questions for?

What does this say about your 'love of neighbor"

# Develop "Connecting Points" Awareness

The Celtic people call these "thin places." They are the times and circumstances in people's lives during which they are more open to the loving support of a faith community. They are times when the normal barriers recede, and people long for connection with someone who cares:

Marriage

Birth of a child

Moving into a new neighborhood

Divorce

Loss of a loved one

Aging

Health issues

Loss of property

Loss of job.

There are many more connecting points. It is helpful to teach regular attenders about these opportunities to engage people in meaningful ways.

How could your congregation help people understand these opportunities and be equipped to meet them? For example, the Stephen Ministry training is a great resource.

Build a SMART goal and action plan to advance the practices of Incarnational Hospitality using the template provided.

## SMART GOAL WITH "SO THAT " STATEMENT

Ministry: _____   Date: _____

| List Goal statement below: |
| --- |
|  |

WRITE ONE STATEMENT PER PAGE WITH ACTION PLANS BELOW

| WHAT ARE WE DOING? | WHO WILL DO IT? (NAME) | BY WHEN WILL WE COMPLETE THIS TASK? MM/DD/YY | RESOURCES NEEDED | ADDITIONAL COMMENTS |
| --- | --- | --- | --- | --- |
|  |  |  |  |  |
|  |  |  |  |  |
|  |  |  |  |  |
|  |  |  |  |  |
|  |  |  |  |  |
|  |  |  |  |  |
|  |  |  |  |  |
|  |  |  |  |  |
|  |  |  |  |  |
|  |  |  |  |  |
|  |  |  |  |  |
|  |  |  |  |  |
|  |  |  |  |  |
|  |  |  |  |  |

USE ADDITIONAL PAGES AS NEEDED TO CLEARLY COMMUNICATE
YOUR TASK TO ACCOMPLISH THE GOAL

# Shift 2

## From Worship as an Event
## to Worship as a Lifestyle

So here's what I want you to do, God helping you: Take
your everyday, ordinary life—your sleeping, eating,
going-to-work, and walking-around life—and place
it before God as an offering.

**—The Apostle Paul, Romans 12:1 (The Message)**

You are and always will be a worshiper. It's what you do.
You can't help it. You can't stop it. You can't live
without it. But you can choose where you invest it...
We're created to worship.

**—Louie Giglio, The Air I Breathe (1)**

# Worship Survey

The survey for this chapter will help you and your congregation explore the quality of your worship experience. Just having key leaders answer these detailed questions will provide valuable insights, but opening this survey to the entire congregation could be revelatory.

(1 = Poor . . . 4 = Amazing)

| | **Passionate Worship** | 1 | 2 | 3 | 4 |
|---|---|---|---|---|---|
| 1. | I attend worship as often as possible, aiming for a minimum of 3 weekends a month. | | | | |
| 2. | The music in worship inspires and lifts my spirit. It is done with excellence. | | | | |
| 3. | I encounter the presence of God in our regular worship services and am inspired to live more fully in the presence of God. | | | | |
| 4. | Our worship services include active participation of the next generations (young adults, youth, and children). | | | | |
| 5. | Worship services are designed to be attractive and engaging for the next generations. | | | | |
| 6. | The worship messages are practical and relevant to my everyday life and encourage me to take next steps in my discipleship journey. | | | | |
| 7. | The worship design enhances my personal worship practices through the introduction of new disciplines and experiences. | | | | |
| 8. | The focus of worship is not disrupted by lengthy stretches of announcements. | | | | |

| | | 1 | 2 | 3 | 4 |
|---|---|---|---|---|---|
| 9. | The lessons of Scripture are often presented in creative ways that engage my spirit. | | | | |
| 10. | I leave every worship experience with a clear sense of something I can do to live more fully as a disciple of Jesus Christ. | | | | |
| 11. | I understand the ways in which my offering is making a difference in the community and people's lives. | | | | |
| 12. | Worship experiences are designed in such a way that my senses (sight, sound, touch, smell) are engaged as well as my mind. | | | | |
| 13. | Worship is led by a team including both lay persons and clergy. | | | | |
| 14. | Each worship experience is based on a theme, and every element of worship is designed to bring new levels of understanding. | | | | |
| 15. | The preacher in our worship service shares the message without notes while walking around. | | | | |
| 16. | I regularly feel engaged by the worship experience rather than part of an audience in worship. | | | | |
| 17. | Every worship experience gives me the opportunity to commit more of my life to Jesus. | | | | |
| 18. | The main points of the worship experience are presented so creatively I recall them even weeks later. | | | | |
| 19. | Guests are greeted warmly in worship yet given permission to remain anonymous if desired. | | | | |
| 20. | At some point in each worship experience, I am engaged physically. | | | | |
| 21. | Persons in the congregation make it a point to engage people they don't know in conversation following worship. | | | | |

|  |  | 1 | 2 | 3 | 4 |
|---|---|---|---|---|---|
| 22. | Each worship experience gives clear next steps in my journey as a disciple. |  |  |  |  |
| 23. | The design of the worship service provides opportunities to develop new personal spiritual practices. |  |  |  |  |
| 24. | Any announcements made during worship provide an opportunity for me to be engaged in the ministry of the congregation. |  |  |  |  |
| 25. | Technical support in the worship experience is done with excellence and creativity. |  |  |  |  |

A perfect score on this survey would be 100 points.

When using this with your leadership team or congregation, here is how you determine an average score:

Total the points for each individual survey. Add the points from all the individual surveys together. Divide that total number by the number of surveys that were completed. This gives you an average score (out of 100 possible points), providing you with a "grade" for your congregational health in this area. Using a standard academic scale:

$$90+ \quad = \quad A$$
$$80\text{-}89 \quad = \quad B$$
$$70\text{-}79 \quad = \quad C$$
$$60\text{-}69 \quad = \quad D$$

What grade does your worship receive? What did the survey reveal? What is your strongest area? What do you hope for in worship? Write your answers in the space below.

# TEAM ACTIVITY!

Mystery Worshiper Audit: One of the best ways to get a strong sense of how well your congregation is doing with the worship experience is to have a couple of people from outside the congregation come and worship with you and provide insights from their experience. The following tool is designed to help that process:

## Mystery Worship Audit

### Instructions

Please complete this audit as you visit a new church. Or have "mystery shoppers" visit your church and do the audit for you.

Your age_____

Your gender_____

Church_____

Name_____

Preacher_____

Please rate your experience of each item:
3 = excellent, 2 = adequate, 1 = needs improvement, N/A = not applicable

### Welcome and Hospitality

_____ Was it easy to find a parking spot and entrance door – was the signage adequate?

_____ Was the church handicapped accessible?

_____ Were you greeted at door by an usher or greeter who helped you find the nursery, restrooms or sanctuary?

_____ Did a member of the congregation engage you in a conversation seeking to get to know you and your needs?

_____ Was the church clean and inviting?

_____ Did the worship schedule offer options and variety?

**Comments on Welcome and Hospitality:**

_____

_____

_____

_____

**Worship:**

_____ Could you follow the worship service, if you were non-religious or visiting?

_____ Did the service flow from one element to the next?

_____ Did you feel engaged and included in the worship experience?

_____ Were the use of bulletins and multimedia effective, including size of print?

_____ Was the theme of the service apparent in music, hymns, prayers, children's story, etc.?

_____ Was the sermon well delivered and easy to understand?

_____ Could you apply the sermon to your everyday life?

_____ Were you offered a challenge or time of decision-making as a follow up to sermon?

_____ Was there laity participation in the service?

_____ Was there a good balance between celebration and reflection?

_____ Was the worship environment positive and conducive to worship?

_____ Did anything make you feel excluded, unwelcome, stupid, or second class?

_____ If it was a communion Sunday, did you feel like you were invited to the table and was the process explained?

_____ Was the music program well prepared and of good quality?

## Comments on Worship:

_____

_____

_____

_____

## Children's Ministries:

_____ If you have a child who needed nursery or bathroom, did someone offer to hel you find them?

_____ Was it easy to determine what was available for your child, either nursery or children's ministry?

_____ Did you use the nursery?

_____ Was that a good experience?

_____ Did you feel safe sending your children to children's ministry or nursery?

## Comments on Children's Ministries:

_____

_____

_____

_____

## Post Worship Time:

_____ Were you greeted by the pastor or other members at the end of worship?

_____ Was there a special fellowship time with refreshments?

_____ Were you invited to fellowship time by other members and did folks engage you in conversation?

_____ Did you leave knowing that there were opportunities for you to serve, either in   ministry or mission?

_____ Was there a visitor card or another method of communication to allow for visitor follow-up?

_____ Did someone send you a welcome letter or phone you after you visited the church?

_____ Is the bulletin written for attracting new worshippers, not using insider language which a visitor would not understand?

_____ Would you come back to this church? Why or why not?

_____

_____

_____

_____

## Comments on Post Worship Time:

_____

_____

_____

_____

_____

_This survey is available as a free download from emc3coaching.com, located under the Resources tab._

# Guiding Principle

**Worship fills the longing of our soul and the desire
of God's heart as we encounter the living God.**

# *EPIC Worship*

**E**xperiential · **P**articipatory · **I**mage-Driven · **C**onnective

# TEAM ACTIVITY!

God's Story: It's a simple exercise. Take your bulletin with
the regular order of worship and make the call! Is this congregational logistics or is this focused on worshiping God?

| Worship Elements | Yes | No | |
|---|---|---|---|
| Welcome | | | |
| Announcements | | | |
| Greeting Time | | | |
| Songs | | | |
| Prayers | | | |
| Scripture | | | |
| Message | | | |
| Offering | | | |
| Communion | | | |
| Next Steps | | | |
| Benediction | | | |

What surprised you as you considered this?

In the last column (unlabeled), estimate the amount of time spent on
the things that you identified as not being worship focused. What
percentage of your average worship service do these represent?

*Shift 2.0* presents a couple of "rules" for announcements:

- 3 in 3: three announcements in 3 minutes or less
- 80%: any announcement made must impact at least 80% of the people gathered.

How does your congregation limit the time spent on announcements and decide what will be offered in worship and what would be better presented in a different way?

Worship is centered around understanding the ways God has been at work throughout human history. It is God's story. It is also a time when we discover our place in that story and claim that story as our own.

## Creating an EPIC Experience (GPS)

Leonard Sweet, author and former seminary dean, uses the framework of EPIC to describe well-designed worship:

- Experiential
- Participatory
- Image Rich
- Connective.

## Experiential (God-Centered)

Research by the Barna Group reports that a very small percentage of those who attend weekend worship experiences indicate that they have experienced the presence of God during corporate worship over the past year.

Experiential worship delights in the presence of God. It is a reminder that our faith is not just a set of beliefs to be remembered but a relationship to be experienced. The Bible is a good reminder of this. It is not a book primarily about what people believed about God. It is the story of the experiences/relationship of individuals and communities with God.

How do the elements of your worship gathering invite people to experience the presence of God?

## Participatory

It is the desire of God's heart that we offer our worship. It is also the longing of our souls. Not just to come to worship but to be engaged in worship. How does your worship engage people (emotionally, spiritually, physically)?

Yes, even physically; not just standing up or sitting down or singing. In working with congregations across the country, one of the key factors in people identifying that they had experienced the presence of God in worship was physical engagement of some type. For example, when asked to specifically identify a worship service in which they felt God's presence. participants routinely listed one or more of the following:

- Christmas Eve (candle-light)
- Ash Wednesday
- Holy Communion
- Laying on of hands for prayer
- Anointing with oil for healing
- Maundy Thursday
- Candle prayer altars
- Baptism.

The common element is the physical connection. People experience God's presence in the act of engaging physically.

How could your worship be designed to include more physical connections?

## Image-Driven (Sensory)

Strong worship experiences also engage the whole person, connecting with all of our senses:

- Hearing
- Seeing
- Smelling
- Touching
- Tasting.

When have you experienced the engaging of your senses in worship?

## Connective

There's a reason we gather as community to worship. While personal worship experiences are helpful, and personal retreats are formational, the community gathered for worship is transformational. Consider the following opportunities of corporate worship:

- Experience the presence of God
- Invitation to become a disciple of Jesus
- Personal transformation
- Presentation of clear next steps as a disciple
- Training for a lifestyle of worship
- Re-membering the Body of Christ.

In the "Fellowship to Hospitality" portion of this guide we talked about the importance of relationships. Worship is a time where we can grow in our relationship with God, grow in our relationship with each other, and grow in our commitment to engage the community around us.

In a world filled with pseudo-relationships (hundreds of friends we've never spoken to and snippets of life shared without any involvement), the church can model a better way of doing life. Life is better done together. We are designed to do life together.

How does your worship encourage deeper relational connections?

- Do you provide space for relational connections (i.e. a hospitality center)?
- Does your greeting time provide an opportunity to get to know someone or is it a rushed 'meet and greet'?
- Do you pray for the people or encourage them to pray for each other?

You get the idea!

How does your worship experience provide welcome for the stranger in your midst? The development of interpersonal relationships? The recognition of significant moments of celebration or concern? Build a SMART goal and action plan to advance your ideas for ways to create EPIC worship.

## SMART GOAL WITH "SO THAT " STATEMENT

Ministry: _____ Date: _____

| List Goal statement below: |
|---|
|  |
|  |
|  |

WRITE ONE STATEMENT PER PAGE WITH ACTION PLANS BELOW

| WHAT ARE WE DOING? | WHO WILL DO IT? (NAME) | BY WHEN WILL WE COMPLETE THIS TASK? MM/DD/YY | RESOURCES NEEDED | ADDITIONAL COMMENTS |
|---|---|---|---|---|
|  |  |  |  |  |
|  |  |  |  |  |
|  |  |  |  |  |
|  |  |  |  |  |
|  |  |  |  |  |
|  |  |  |  |  |
|  |  |  |  |  |
|  |  |  |  |  |
|  |  |  |  |  |
|  |  |  |  |  |
|  |  |  |  |  |
|  |  |  |  |  |
|  |  |  |  |  |
|  |  |  |  |  |
|  |  |  |  |  |
|  |  |  |  |  |

USE ADDITIONAL PAGES AS NEEDED TO CLEARLY COMMUNICATE
YOUR TASK TO ACCOMPLISH THE GOAL

# Guiding Principle

**Worship is bigger than a weekly event. Worship is
about a lifestyle through which we bring glory
and honor to God in all that we do.**

## Encouraging Personal Worship

In the *Shift 2.0* book, a guide for having a personal devotional time is presented. How does your congregation encourage personal worship? For example:

- Is the congregation encouraged through weekly worship messages to have a personal devotional time?
- Are resources provided to support a devotional time?
- Do you train people in an introductory class on spiritual practices how to have a personal devotional time?
- Do you offer testimonies about how people have been blessed in their devotional time?
- Are classes in spiritual practices offered to expose people to a wide variety of disciplines?
- How are people encouraged to engage in serving others as a form of worship?

## Corporate worship as training for personal worship

The weekly corporate worship event serves as a great opportunity to equip people for growth in their personal worship time. *Shift 2.0* presents several ways to build this training into the worship experience. For example:

- Teaching various prayer frameworks through modeling a prayer during the pastoral or corporate prayer time.
- Introducing people to a variety of methods for studying

51

the Scriptures in the "Reading of God's Word" part of the service.

- Modeling interpersonal hospitality in the way that greeting times are presented.

Every element of worship has the potential to equip people for worship. How could your congregation be equipped in worship (the best opportunity you have to reach the most people)?

## Clear Next Steps

Worship has a strong discipleship component. Messages that impact people's' lives are relevant and practical, and conclude with a clear next step in people's discipleship journey. This may be accomplished in a variety of forms:

- A question
- An invitation
- A challenge.

Whatever form it takes, how does your worship provide clarity about next steps in the discipleship journey? Build a SMART goal and action plan to advance your ideas for ways to encourage personal worship.

# SMART GOAL WITH "SO THAT " STATEMENT

Ministry: _____ Date: _____

List Goal statement below:

WRITE ONE STATEMENT PER PAGE WITH ACTION PLANS BELOW

| WHAT ARE WE DOING? | WHO WILL DO IT? (NAME) | BY WHEN WILL WE COMPLETE THIS TASK? MM/DD/YY | RESOURCES NEEDED | ADDITIONAL COMMENTS |
|---|---|---|---|---|
| | | | | |
| | | | | |
| | | | | |
| | | | | |
| | | | | |
| | | | | |
| | | | | |
| | | | | |
| | | | | |
| | | | | |
| | | | | |
| | | | | |
| | | | | |
| | | | | |
| | | | | |

USE ADDITIONAL PAGES AS NEEDED TO CLEARLY COMMUNICATE
YOUR TASK TO ACCOMPLISH THE GOAL

# Guiding Principle

**God deserves the best we have to offer.**

## Worship Planning

Consider the following questions with your team:

- Who is involved in worship planning?
- How far ahead do we plan?
- How much time is spent on worship planning?
- How much communication is there among worship leaders?
- How does our planning take into account those we are seeking to reach?
- How does our worship impact the various dimensions of discipleship?

It's no secret. The hour of weekend worship is the greatest opportunity of the pastor and church to invite people to find themselves in God's story and take the next step in their journey. It is an amazing privilege to have this hour of undivided attention from your congregation.

How will you use this gift?

There are some best practices gleaned from those pastors and congregations that are growing and making an impact on their communities:

- They spend significant time in planning for worship, both long-term and weekly.
- They prepare extensively for each worship experience.
- They regularly evaluate the effectiveness of the worship experience and revise accordingly.

- They recognize and plan for worship that invites growth in discipleship.

How well do these best practices describe your situation?

## Creative Worship Design

Our God is a creative God and, as those created in God's image, we are a creative people. We are also more connected, engaged, and transformed when we are invited into God's story in creative ways. A rule of thumb: Whatever you want people to remember must be presented in the most creative way possible.

So, what can you do to present the amazing truths of God's Word in ways that capture the imagination of the people sitting in worship? The following page presents some ideas to get you started.

## ASTHETICS

- Banners with theme of message series.
- Creative altar design.
- Backdrops for skits (e.g. historical scenes, bridge).
- Gathering Area/Narthex design.
- Use of children's drawings and paintings in gathering area/worship space.

## PRINTED MATERIALS

- Bulletin cover with message theme highlighted.
- QR code in bulletin.
- Newsletter themed with articles related to message series.
- Devotional guides for families related to series.
- Discussion guides for small groups.
- Take-Away reflections and next steps from message.
- Take-Away info for co-workers or neighbors with series info.

## SIGNAGE

- Marquee on church sign related to message series.
- Art displayed in entryway/worship center.

## MUSICAL SELECTIONS

- All music for worship should reinforce the message theme.
- Worship leader may introduce with story or scripture.
- Intentional focus on congregational music being "sing-able."
- Flash-Mob Choir opportunities for children, youth, and adults.

## MEDIA

- Video selections related to theme/illustrating theme – used in message or welcome time.
- Powerpoint slides with image that reinforces the message theme.
- Moving backgrounds or other static imagery reinforcing the message.
- Incorporate children, youth, and adult art through scanning to digital media.
- Website with theme image for series.
- Facebook check-in with announcements or call to worship.
- Encourage tweeting sermon with use of hashtag for worship.
- Encourage prayer texts from worship to friends/family.
- Capturing testimonies and ministry areas on video to allow a "window" into new opportunities and touched lives.

## DRAMA/EXPERIENTIAL

- Skits developing message theme.
- Testimonies/witnesses.
- Message.
- Next steps following message.
- Sacraments – tied to theme.
- Prayer teams/healing and anointing – tied to theme.
- Poetry.
- Health kits for UMCOR assembled during the service; praying over lives that will be touched by ministry.

## LITURGY

- Scripture selections.
- Prayers that reinforce theme.
- Dramatic readings.
- Psalms.
- Video liturgy.

## SUPPLEMENTARY

- Materials, such as recommended books at Welcome Center.

Creative worship design includes all dimensions of the worship experience. This is a good place to remind you that the worship service is the message, not just the sermon (message) portion. Everything about the worship experience should communicate the same theme.

So, how can creative worship design be applied to all the dimensions of worship? Let's look at some examples:

- Altar arrangements that provide a visual connection to the theme:

  ○ variety of breads from different cultures on World Communion Sunday

  ○ sandals arrangement to communicate service or following in the footsteps of Jesus

  ○ ball and chain to communicate the weight of slavery to debt or sin

  ○ candles representing the presence of God or invitation to prayer

- Banners, projected images, original artwork focused on theme of worship

- Prayer circles in place of corporate prayer

- Drama presentations of themes

- Video interviews focused on theme or testimony for offering.

You get the idea! Be creative.

*Shift 2.0* presents a couple of approaches to worship design, including the 4-MAT model and a more traditional planning guide approach.

How is worship planning done in your setting? Who is involved? How could more creativity be involved in the worship design?

Remember, worship that is done well shares these qualities:

- Central theme

- Creative presentation

- Clear next steps for discipleship
- Engagement of the body as well as the mind.

At the heart of all of this is what Dave Ferguson calls The Big Idea. This refers to worship in which all elements are built around that central theme. This means everything.

For example, if the theme is *serving one another:*

- Announcements are focused on opportunities to serve.
- The welcome to worship celebrates the call to serve.
- The songs have a servant theme.
- The prayer includes a reference to opening us up to the needs of others.
- The scripture is focused on a story of someone serving.
- The message gives practical help on living into our call to serve.
- Communion celebrates the One who serves us at the table and empowers us to serve.
- The Benediction sends people out to serve.

## Worship Teams

*Shift 2.0* recommends that Creative Worship Design be done by a Creative Worship Design Team. Long gone are the days when the full responsibility for worship design fell to the pastor. The teams do not need to be large, and they do not need to be staff-driven. The primary selection criteria for this team should be a creative spirit and a longing for passionate worship.

# GETTING THE MOST BENEFIT
## FROM YOUR TEAM

| | PASTOR | TEAM |
|---|---|---|
| 6 Month Planning Guide | Prepare planning guide document:<br>• Themes<br>• Scriptures<br>• Brief description | Research begins:<br>• Articles/data<br>• Illustrations<br>• Video clips<br>• Skits / dramatic readings<br>• Banners for message series |
| 1 Month Planning Guide | Outline of message and proposed illustration. | Team builds creative elements |
| 2 Week Planning Guide | Design of worship service experience (each is unique to theme). | Special teams as needed:<br>• Video<br>• Powerpoints / media<br>• Drama<br>• Altar design |
| 1 Week Planning Guide | Draft of message manuscript presented to team for review, discussion, editing. | Spreadsheet is prepared for worship services outlining timing, activity, person responsible, lighting, media, and sound requirements. |
| Critiquing the Experience | Pastor and team review the worship experience from the previous week. | • What worked well?<br>• What needed improvement?<br>• What have we learned? |

How does your church plan worship? How might a team support the creative process? Build a SMART goal and action plan to strengthen your worship design process.

## Guiding Principle

**Worship style should meet the needs of the community in which God has placed the church.**

## TEAM ACTIVITY!

**Different strokes for different folks:** From the listing of common worship elements found below circle the one that is most meaningful to you and be prepared to describe why.

- Gathering
  - Welcome
  - Greeting
  - Songs of Praise
  - Prayers
  - Confession
- Proclamation
  - Scripture reading
  - Message
- Response to the Word
  - Tithes and offerings
  - Communion
  - Prayer
  - Commitment
- Sending Forth
  - Songs
  - Next steps
  - Benediction

Take a moment and let each person share the element of worship they selected and briefly explain why that is the most meaningful to them. The chances are very good that not all of you selected the same element. For a wide variety of reasons, people are touched by different things in worship.

The same is true for the people who live in the community around the church.

Most of the time the driving factor for determining the style of worship engaged by a congregation seems to be the preferences of the current worshiping congregation. That would be fine if the church existed to meet the needs of those already there.

But, our *Book of Discipline* is very clear.

> The church of Jesus Christ exists in and for the world...
> The church is a strategic base from which Christians
> move out to the structures of society...to help people
> accept and confess Jesus Christ as Lord and Savior...**the
> local church is to minister to persons in the commu-
> nity where the church is located...**

—**Paragraph 204,** *Book of Discipline,* **United Methodist Church (emphasis added)**

The church doesn't exist for those who are already there. It exists to reach the people out in the community.

Worship is one way that this is accomplished.

**What if we switched the question from . . .**

- What do you like or dislike about our current worship experience?

**to**

- What kind of worship experience would we need to provide to reach the people in our surrounding community?

The answer to the second question can only be found by understanding the demographics of your community. In the "Fellowship to Hospitality" section, we introduced the tool called MissionInsite QuickInsite Report. That report contained information about Mosaic or Lifestyle Groups in your community and the level of representation.

Also available through MissionInsite is a tool from Thomas Bandy identifying the preferences of each Mosaic Group in a variety of things, including worship style. Using these resources, consider the following table of worship styles. Find the one that best represents your congregation and then the one that best represents the demographic group you are trying to connect with. How well do they line up?

Build a SMART goal and action plan to explore ways in which your worship services could connect more strongly to the specific needs of your community.

## SMART GOAL WITH "SO THAT " STATEMENT

Ministry: _____  Date: _____

List Goal statement below:

WRITE ONE STATEMENT PER PAGE WITH ACTION PLANS BELOW

| WHAT ARE WE DOING? | WHO WILL DO IT? (NAME) | BY WHEN WILL WE COMPLETE THIS TASK? MM/DD/YY | RESOURCES NEEDED | ADDITIONAL COMMENTS |
|---|---|---|---|---|
| | | | | |
| | | | | |
| | | | | |
| | | | | |
| | | | | |
| | | | | |
| | | | | |
| | | | | |
| | | | | |
| | | | | |
| | | | | |
| | | | | |
| | | | | |
| | | | | |
| | | | | |

USE ADDITIONAL PAGES AS NEEDED TO CLEARLY COMMUNICATE
YOUR TASK TO ACCOMPLISH THE GOAL

# Guiding Principle

**Worship is not a stand-alone event. It is part of a larger system of discipleship and is supported by other dimensions.**

# Authentic Relationships

**As noted previously, most people come to visit a church (usually in a worship experience) because someone invited them. There are several factors that will determine whether they will come, whether they will come back, and whether they will become regular participants in your faith community:**

People come because they trust the friend that invited them due to the relationship that has been established.

People come back because they were intentionally welcomed by the congregation.

People will stay if they develop strong relationships with people in the congregation.

These themes are given much fuller treatment in the "Fellowship to Hospitality" section of this Activation Guide.

## Welcoming Congregations

Most people decide if they are going to come to the church for a second visit within 7 minutes of the time they arrive on the church property. That means they probably have not heard your wonderful musical group or the amazing message from your pastor before they decide.

The deciding factor for a return visit is how welcoming the congregation is. Are the Platform Level things in place to at least make sure people are greeted? Is the congregation trained to personally engage in conversation with guests? Does someone besides the pastor make an effort to get to know them?

The answer to those questions largely determines whether someone will return a 2nd time.

## Relational Connections

If people do choose to come for a second visit, what kind of connections are made? Does the pastor or a key lay person arrange for a connecting interview? Are there follow-up letters or calls? Is there an opportunity provided to connect with a group that likes to do the same things as them?

## Service Engagement

How are people invited to find a way to plug-in? What service opportunities within the church are available for people who want to get connected?

If you want to get people engaged in the life of your church, there are three things that need to happen:

- Personal relationship

- Regular worship

- Service in the church.

Service is also a way to build relationships with others in the church.

## Facilities

Just like we prepare for guests in our homes, the church also ought to prepare for guests. That means:

- Clean and inviting facilities

- Hallways clear of discarded items

- Clean restrooms

- Clear signage to worship, restrooms, and classrooms

- Hospitality center with refreshments.

Reference the facility assessment you completed in the "Fellowship to Hospitality" section.

## Childcare

The quality of childcare provided is a huge factor in engaging young families in your church. The nursery should be located as close to the sanctuary as possible. It should be bright and clean. It should be professionally staffed. There should be a system for notifying parents should there be a problem. Clear check-in and pick-up procedures must be established. Safe sanctuary policies must be followed.

Build a SMART goal and action plan to advance your ideas for ways to support the worship experience by paying attention to congregational experiences surrounding the actual worship service.

# SMART GOAL WITH "SO THAT " STATEMENT

Ministry: _____ Date: _____

| List Goal statement below: |
| --- |
| |
| |
| |

WRITE ONE STATEMENT PER PAGE WITH ACTION PLANS BELOW

| WHAT ARE WE DOING? | WHO WILL DO IT? (NAME) | BY WHEN WILL WE COMPLETE THIS TASK? MM/DD/YY | RESOURCES NEEDED | ADDITIONAL COMMENTS |
| --- | --- | --- | --- | --- |
| | | | | |
| | | | | |
| | | | | |
| | | | | |
| | | | | |
| | | | | |
| | | | | |
| | | | | |
| | | | | |
| | | | | |
| | | | | |
| | | | | |
| | | | | |

USE ADDITIONAL PAGES AS NEEDED TO CLEARLY COMMUNICATE
YOUR TASK TO ACCOMPLISH THE GOAL

# Shift 3

## From Membership to Discipleship

I have been crucified with Christ and I no longer live,
but Christ lives in me.

**—The Apostle Paul, Galatians 2:20**

[S]o that we may no longer be children. . .

Rather, speaking the truth in love, we are to grow up
in every way into him who is the head, into Christ.

**—The Apostle Paul, Ephesians 4:14-15 (ESV)**

"Come, follow me. . ."

**—Jesus, Matthew 4:19 (NIV)**

"Therefore go and make disciples . . . teaching them to
obey everything I have commanded you."

**—Jesus, Matthew 28:19–20 (NIV)**

# Discipleship Survey

A survey to be completed by leadership and congregation members to evaluate the quality of discipleship within your church. After reading the statement to the left, rate your response from 1-4 with 4 representing strong agreement and 1 representing disagreement.

(1 = Poor....4= Amazing)

| | Intentional Discipleship | 1 | 2 | 3 | 4 |
|---|---|---|---|---|---|
| 1 | This congregation has established clear expectations for maturity in discipleship. | | | | |
| 2. | I am an active participant in a small group that includes fellowship, growth, and mission experiences. | | | | |
| 3. | At least once a year, someone from the congregation has a conversation with me about my progress as a disciple. | | | | |
| 4. | Our congregation offers a variety of educational experiences based on the level of maturity as a disciple. | | | | |
| 5. | I have spiritual friends, a mentor, a coach, or a spiritual director who holds me accountable. | | | | |
| 6. | Lay persons are equipped to lead small groups and serve as mentors or coaches for discipleship. | | | | |
| 7. | Worship experiences consistently lead persons to the next step in their discipleship. | | | | |
| 8. | The most mature disciples are encouraged to provide discipling relationships with those new to the faith and leadership for the ministries of the congregation. | | | | |
| 9. | I am involved in serving in the local community, making a difference in people's lives. | | | | |
| 10. | I take responsibility for my own spiritual growth through the daily practices of spiritual disciplines. | | | | |

| | | | | | |
|---|---|---|---|---|---|
| 11. | I have relationships beyond the local church through which I am intentionally sharing God's love. | | | | |
| 12. | I give 10% of my income to the ministry of the local church and seek to honor God with the rest. | | | | |
| 13. | I have one or more close friends participating in worship and ministry with me at this church. | | | | |
| 14. | The church has helped me in understanding the Bible and how its teaching applies to my life. | | | | |
| 15. | The leaders of this congregation have such a close walk with Jesus that I am inspired to follow them. | | | | |
| 16. | I really feel like I belong to this community of faith. I am valued, loved, and engaged. | | | | |
| 17. | I am growing in my relationship with Jesus through my connection to this community of faith. | | | | |
| 18. | I have clarity about how God has gifted and called me to serve (made possible through a guided exploration process). | | | | |
| 19. | I live within financial margins in order to bless other people more. | | | | |
| 20. | This congregation helps beginning disciples learn how to pray, read the Bible, and serve. | | | | |
| 21. | Leaders for this congregation are drawn from the most spiritually mature disciples. | | | | |
| 22. | There is training available for this congregation in the building of healthy relationships and sharing faith. | | | | |
| 23. | There is a clear vision of what this congregation hopes for with every disciple engaged in the community of faith. | | | | |
| 24. | While a wide variety of classes are offered, there is also a core curriculum leading people toward the vision for discipleship. | | | | |
| 25. | I am discovering more and more the depths of Jesus' love and longings for me as a disciple. | | | | |

A perfect score on this survey would be 100 points.

When using this with your leadership team or congregation, here is how you determine an average score: Total the points for each individual survey. Add the points from all the individual surveys together. Divide that total number by the number of surveys that were completed. This gives you an average score (out of 100 possible points), providing you with a "grade" for your congregational health in this area. Using a standard academic scale:

$$90+ \quad = \quad A$$
$$80\text{-}89 \quad = \quad B$$
$$70\text{-}79 \quad = \quad C$$
$$60\text{-}69 \quad = \quad D$$

What grade does your congregational discipleship receive? What did the survey reveal? What is your strongest area? What do you hope for in creating an intentional discipleship process?

# Guiding Principle

**Begin with the end in mind.**

# Team Activity!

**Defining Discipleship:** Divide your team into pairs or triads. Give each smaller group a sheet of newsprint and a 'fat' Sharpie marker.

Ask them to write on their newsprint what it means to be a disciple. What does a disciple look like? What does a disciple do?

Let each group present their results.

What did your team discover? Did everyone agree on the same points? Is there a sense of clarity?

*Shift 2.0* presents a definition for discipleship that looks like this:

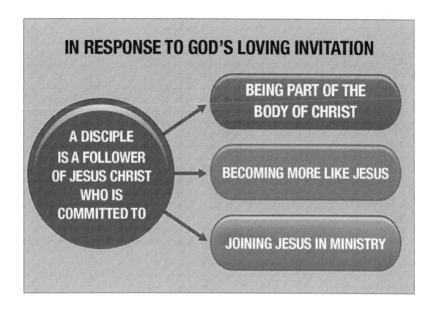

Biblically, it is represented by Matthew 4:19:

> "Come, follow me," Jesus said, "and I will
> make you fishers of men."

*Come, follow me:* Being Part of the Body of Christ
*I will make you:* Becoming more like Jesus
*Fishers of men:* Joining Jesus in ministry

The vision for maturing discipleship in *Shift 2.0* is:

# WOULD OUR CHURCHES BE
## *More vital? More effective? More transforming?*
### If people...

- Lived lives honoring God in the ways they worked, played, engaged others?
- Intentionally built relationships in order to be Christ to someone?
- Took responsibility for their own spiritual growth?
- Discipled someone else, helping them move toward maturity?
- Used their gifts and talents to serve others?
- Lived within margins in order to bless others ?

What is the vision of your congregation for maturing discipleship? What are you hoping for in the lives of disciples in your congregation?

Based on your own experience and particular point of view, what do you like about these descriptions?

How would your team change these descriptions?

What would your team add to these descriptions?

How do you communicate that vision?

There are lots of ways to do this.  Consider the following:

- Discipleship preaching/teaching series
- Maturing discipleship illustrations in weekly messages during worship
- Testimonies from maturing disciples about the difference they are experiencing
- Blogs
- Newsletter messages
- Brochures
- Banners
- Small group focus.

One of the best ways to communicate a definition for discipleship is to establish a membership covenant.  This provides a clarity of expectations centered around the practices of maturing disciples.  Here's an example of such a covenant:

| Traditional Vows | Dimensions of Discipleship | Membership Covenant |
|---|---|---|
| Prayers | Opening to Jesus/ Obeying Jesus | Participate regularly in a small discipleship group or other accountable discipling relationship. |
| Presence | A Life of Worship | Participate in weekly worship at least 3 weekends each month unless prevented by illness or travel. |
| Gifts | A Life of Generosity | Commit to proportional giving to the ministries of this congregation and to moving toward a tithe. |
| Service | A Life of Service | Serve in some way in the local community (beyond the walls of the church) each month. |
| Witness | A Life of Hospitality | Invite someone to come with me to church/events at least three times per year and build at least three relationships outside the church to witness the love of Christ. |

Gallup research notes that if you want people to be engaged in the life and ministry of your faith community, you need to be clear about expectations.

All churches have some unwritten expectations: show up in worship, give to the church, help with projects as needed.

What are your expectations? Are they clearly identified? How are they communicated?

## Building the Foundation

### Discerning the Current Reality

The starting point for moving forward toward the 'end' goal of maturing disciples is to figure out where the congregation is currently. There are a couple of tools that are helpful in this:

# Team Activity!

Missional Vital Signs: There are several signs of vitality that most congregations track (and all United Methodists). These are called Missional Vital Signs. They include average worship participation, affirmations of faith, number of people in small groups, and annual financial support for the congregation (not capital campaigns).

The data for the number of people in small groups is helpful in a couple of ways. The following graphic is a sample of this in a graph form.

First, look at the 10-year trend. Is it increasing or decreasing? By what percentage?

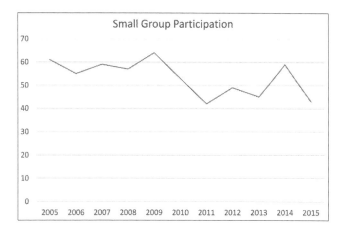

In the graph above a 30% decline in small group participation is indicated. Why is this significant?

- Small groups are the primary point of connection for growing relationships in the congregation.
- Small groups are the centerpiece of most discipleship processes.

Next, calculate the percentage of persons represented in small groups based on the average worship participation.

The average worship participation for this sample church is currently 140. There are 40 persons participating in small groups. This means that 28.6% of the congregation is involved in small groups.

Research indicates that it is almost a guarantee (as close as we can call it) that when a congregation reaches and goes beyond

50% participation in small groups, the church is growing.

- What is the trend for small group participation in your congregation?

- What percentage of the congregation are involved in small groups?

- While small groups participation is not an actual measurement of the level of discipleship, it is a key indicator.

For a more accurate look at the overall level of maturity in discipleship for your congregation, the Real Discipleship Survey is recommended (a detailed evaluative tool referenced in *Shift 2.0* and available at emc3coaching.com). This gives insight into the level of maturity (exploring, beginning, growing, and maturing) for six key dimensions of the discipleship journey:

- A Life of Worship
- A Life of Hospitality
- A Life Opening to Jesus
- A Life Obeying Jesus
- A Life of Service
- A Life of Generosity.

As you review the matrix indicating the percentage of people placing themselves in each level of maturity or each dimension, what did you discover about the current reality of your congregation? Where are the demonstrated gaps in your discipleship process?

Build a SMART goal and action plan to advance your ideas for closing the gaps and giving your congregation the tools for becoming more mature disciples.

## SMART GOAL WITH "SO THAT " STATEMENT

Ministry: _____ Date: _____

List Goal statement below:

WRITE ONE STATEMENT PER PAGE WITH ACTION PLANS BELOW

| WHAT ARE WE DOING? | WHO WILL DO IT? (NAME) | BY WHEN WILL WE COMPLETE THIS TASK? MM/DD/YY | RESOURCES NEEDED | ADDITIONAL COMMENTS |
|---|---|---|---|---|
| | | | | |
| | | | | |
| | | | | |
| | | | | |
| | | | | |
| | | | | |
| | | | | |
| | | | | |
| | | | | |
| | | | | |
| | | | | |
| | | | | |
| | | | | |

USE ADDITIONAL PAGES AS NEEDED TO CLEARLY COMMUNICATE
YOUR TASK TO ACCOMPLISH THE GOAL

# Guiding Principle

**Every system produces exactly what it is designed to do.**

What is your congregation hoping for people to do/be as disciples
of Jesus?

- Are you hoping that people will pray?
- Are you hoping that people will read their Bibles?
- Are you hoping that people will serve?
- Are you hoping that people will worship?
- Are you hoping that people will give?
- Are you hoping that people will care for one another?
- Are you hoping that people will invite others to church?
- Are you hoping that people will serve in the community?

Many congregations treat discipleship as if it will happen by
accident or by osmosis as people sit in weekend worship.

But the reality is that this isn't the way it works. We see the
evidence of this as worship participation declines, giving levels
drop, conflict develops, and it becomes more and more difficult
to find people to serve.

Discipleship is an intentional process that includes both
knowledge and application.

Disciples are trained to live into the potential God has placed
before us.

The knowledge (information) track of discipleship is the part
most churches have some comfort level in providing, so let's
start there.

*Shift 2.0* presents 4 phases of development in the life of a
disciple. We are reminded that discipleship is a journey as we
move toward maturity/completeness (language of Jesus) or go on
toward perfection (language of John Wesley).

78

Each phase can be supported by intentional training (education/knowledge).

# Exploring:

| Current Reality | Educational Need |
|---|---|
| Not yet a committed disciple. Checking out the church. Decision making time. | Presentation of what it means to be a disciple, implications for life, what it takes to live as a disciple. |

# Beginning:

| Current Reality | Educational Need |
|---|---|
| Making a commitment to be a disciple. Profession of Faith/Baptism. Introduction to basic spiritual practices. Building connections. | Introduction to basic spiritual practices that provide the foundation for growth as a disciple: Devotional time, authentic relationships, study of Scripture, prayer, generosity, witness. |
| | Discernment of how God has wired them for serving others: Passions, spiritual gifts, talents, personality type, life experiences. |

# Growing:

| Current Reality | Educational Need |
|---|---|
| A time of personal development as each dimension in the life of discipleship is explored, deeper understandings attained, and skills put into practice. | Life of Worship: Offering all of life as a 'living sacrifice' to God. |
| | Life of Hospitality: Relational development skills, conflict management, witnessing. |
| | Life Opening to Jesus: Exploration and practice of spiritual disciplines to keep us connected to God. |
| | Life Obeying Jesus: The study and application of Scripture to life. Mentoring/ Apprenticing/ Discipling skills. |

| | |
|---|---|
| | Life of Service: Determining how God has equipped us to serve and practical exploration of possibilities. |
| | Life of Generosity: Biblical financial management. Debt elimination. Life planning. Kingdom impact. |

## Maturing:

| Current Reality | Educational Need |
|---|---|
| Providing leadership in discipleship relationships, church functions, and community impact. | Development of skills in mentoring, apprenticing, coaching for discipleship, and personal leadership.<br><br>Development of leadership skills (including but not limited to): Facilitation, ministry planning, team building, visioning. |

Here is additional material, reproduced from other Phil's *Creating a Discipleship Pathway* workbook, which gives a closer look at how you could flesh out a detailed pathway based on the levels of discipleship maturity.

## Step 4: Building the Christian Education Side of the Discipleship Pathway

Having given thought to building the accountable relationships rail, let's now focus on constructing the parallel Christian Education rail.

The goal for this track is to provide resources for each individual disciple that are appropriate for that disciple's present phase of development. In *Membership to Discipleship* this idea is illustrated in the graphic called the Discipleship Cycle (page 91).

For example, in the Phase 1 Quadrant of the Discipleship Cycle, it is suggested that no formal resourcing take place, since a person in the Phase 1, or "Exploring" phase of discipleship, is not ready for a conventional class. Any equipping for discipleship for this person will take the form of one-on-one conversations about what it means to be a disciple and why becoming a disciple matters.

In the "Beginning" phase it is suggested that the resourcing/equipping of the new disciple be focused around basic Spiritual Practices and an introduction to Christian Beliefs. In the space below, note specific training your congregation offers to new disciples (we've included some of Phil's favorite suggested resources):

| Suggested Training | Similar Kinds of Training Your Church Offers |
|---|---|
| *A Disciple's Path* by Jim Harnish | |
| *Foundations: An Introduction to Spiritual Practices* by Phil Maynard | |
| *Beginnings* by Andy Langford and Mark Ralls | |
| *Alpha Class* by Nicky Gumble | |

Oftentimes, our Christian Education opportunities are formed around the 'newest and greatest' resource that is highlighted in our inbox or the preferences of those in the congregation. There is nothing wrong with offering these resources. However, Phil suggests that we be more intentional in providing training that specifically leads to maturity in each of the dimensions of discipleship. He calls this the core curriculum.

11

## BEGINNING PHASE

| Suggested Training | Similar Kinds of Training Your Church Offers |
|---|---|
| *A Disciple's Path* by Jim Harnish | |
| *Foundations: An Introduction to Spiritual Practices* by Phil Maynard | |
| *Beginnings* by Andy Langford and Mark Ralls | |
| *Alpha Class* by Nicky Gumble | |
| *Following Jesus* by Carolyn Slaughter | |

## GROWING PHASE

### A Life of Worship...

| Suggested Training | Similar Kinds of Training Your Church Offers |
|---|---|
| *An Altar in the World* by Barbara Brown Taylor | |
| *The Unquenchable Worshiper* by Matt Redman | |
| *Worship His Majesty* by Jack Hayford | |
| *Building Worship Bridges* by Cathy Townley, Kay Kotan, and Bishop Bob Farr | |

### A Life of Hospitality...

| Suggested Training | Similar Kinds of Training Your Church Offers |
|---|---|
| *Making Room* by Christine Pohl | |
| *Peace Makers Conflict Study* | |
| *Authentic Community* by Jim van Ypren | |
| *Connect!* by Phil Maynard | |

## A Life Opening to Jesus...

| Suggested Training | Similar Kinds of Training Your Church Offers |
|---|---|
| *Companions in Christ*, available through Upper Room Ministries | |
| *Celebration of Discipline* by Richard Foster | |
| *Devotional Life in the Wesleyan Tradition* by Steve Harper | |
| *Three Simple Rules: A Wesleyan Way of Living* by Reuben P. Job | |

## A Life Obeying Jesus...

| Suggested Training | Similar Kinds of Training Your Church Offers |
|---|---|
| *Eat This Book* by Eugene Peterson | |
| *A Reflective Life* by Ken Gire | |
| *Disciple Bible Study*, available through Cokesbury Bookstore | |
| *Discipleship Coaching Training*, available through EMC3Coaching.com | |

## A Life of Service...

| Suggested Training | Similar Kinds of Training Your Church Offers |
|---|---|
| *SHAPE* by Eric Reese | |
| *PLACE* by JayMcSwain at placeministries.com | |
| *What Every Church Member Should Know About Poverty* by Bill Ehlig and Ruby Payne | |
| *FIT* available through EMC3 Coaching | |

## A Life of Generosity...

| Suggested Training | Similar Kinds of Training Your Church Offers |
|---|---|
| *Financial Peace University* by Dave Ramsey | |
| *Enough* by Adam Hamilton | |
| *Earn, Save, Give: Wesley's Simple Rules for Money* by Jim Harnish | |
| *Not Your Parent's Offering Plate* by J. Clif Christoper | |

Build a SMART goal and action plan to adjust your current discipleship system to more accurately reflect the clear pathway of discipleship on which you want to guide maturing disciples.

## SMART GOAL WITH "SO THAT " STATEMENT

Ministry: _____ Date: _____

List Goal statement below:

WRITE ONE STATEMENT PER PAGE WITH ACTION PLANS BELOW

| WHAT ARE WE DOING? | WHO WILL DO IT? (NAME) | BY WHEN WILL WE COMPLETE THIS TASK? MM/DD/YY | RESOURCES NEEDED | ADDITIONAL COMMENTS |
|---|---|---|---|---|
| | | | | |
| | | | | |
| | | | | |
| | | | | |
| | | | | |
| | | | | |
| | | | | |
| | | | | |
| | | | | |
| | | | | |
| | | | | |

USE ADDITIONAL PAGES AS NEEDED TO CLEARLY COMMUNICATE
YOUR TASK TO ACCOMPLISH THE GOAL

# Guiding Principle

## Discipleship is a contact sport.

Here are some materials, reproduced from other resources, which expand on the ideas for dynamic, partnered discipleship strategies.

Phil calls discipleship a 'contact sport'. This is because discipleship growth happens within the context of accountable relationships. Gaining knowledge about each of the dimensions of discipleship is a good and indispensable thing. Putting that knowledge into practice is what moves the process from educational to transformational. This happens when someone partners with us to help us build a plan and then holds us accountable to that plan.

The book, *Membership to Discipleship*, suggests a variety of types of relationships and indicates where each may be most helpful along the pathway. Consider the following suggestions and note what your congregation already has in place:

### Exploring Phase

| Suggested | In Place |
|---|---|
| One-on-one mentor/apprentice/faith guide for conversations around what it would mean for someone to commit to being a disciple | |

### Beginning Phase

| Suggested | In Place |
|---|---|
| Classes led by a growing/maturing disciple to assist beginning disciples in building the foundations of spiritual practices and basic theological understandings | |

### Growing Phase

| Suggested | In Place |
|---|---|
| Small groups led by maturing disciples helping growing disciples develop skills in each dimension of discipleship. These groups also provide accountability for personal development | |
| Discipleship Coaches to partner with growing disciples as they explore what it means to mature in each dimension, build a plan for development, and provide accountability for progress | |

### Maturing Phase

| Suggested | In Place |
|---|---|
| Discipleship Coaches to partner with maturing disciples as they explore continuing development in spiritual practices and leadership skills | |
| Spiritual Directors to partner with maturing disciples to help them pay attention to God at work in their lives and to discern next steps in their spiritual growth | |

Build a SMART goal and action plan to develop a strategy for developing "discipleship as a contact sport."

## SMART GOAL WITH "SO THAT " STATEMENT

Ministry: _____ Date: _____

List Goal statement below:

WRITE ONE STATEMENT PER PAGE WITH ACTION PLANS BELOW

| WHAT ARE WE DOING? | WHO WILL DO IT? (NAME) | BY WHEN WILL WE COMPLETE THIS TASK? MM/DD/YY | RESOURCES NEEDED | ADDITIONAL COMMENTS |
|---|---|---|---|---|
| | | | | |
| | | | | |
| | | | | |
| | | | | |
| | | | | |
| | | | | |
| | | | | |
| | | | | |
| | | | | |
| | | | | |
| | | | | |
| | | | | |

USE ADDITIONAL PAGES AS NEEDED TO CLEARLY COMMUNICATE
YOUR TASK TO ACCOMPLISH THE GOAL

# Guiding Principle

**The clearer the path, the easier the journey.**

The discipleship pathway (model) developed by John Wesley, founder of the Methodists, is the approach to discipleship that has been most influential in a wide variety of Christian traditions, including the non-denominational churches.

It brings together the educational focus presented in these materials along with the relational focus just described. These are tied together by the practice of accountability much as the railroad ties keep the two rails stable and functioning.

In a simplified version, this pathway can be presented graphically:

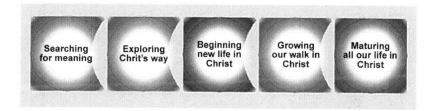

| Phase | Wesley's Process | Contemporary Applications | Relational/Educational |
|---|---|---|---|
| Searching | Community Service and Field Preaching | Attractional events, building relationships, & community service | N/A |
| Exploring | Society Meetings — Preaching Houses (worship) | Corporate worship (small groups and service opportunities are also great connecting points) | One-on-one relational connections with guests/visitors |
| Beginning | Class Meeting — training in basic Christian practices | Foundations Class: Spiritual Practices and Christian Beliefs | Teacher/Facilitator<br><br>Mentors could be used in place of a class |
| Growing | Bands — deep accountable relationships building maturity in living life as a disciple in all dimensions | Small Groups providing training and accountability | Small Groups and Discipleship Coaches<br><br>Training and development around dimensions of discipleship in core curriculum |
| Maturing | Select Societies — equipping leaders to become Society Preachers, Class Leaders, Band Leaders, Ministry Leaders | Very small groups/ one-on-one training for Leadership | Apprentices Mentors Discipleship Coaches Spiritual Directors |

Use the SMART goal and action plan to explore how these elements of a discipling process are represented in your congregation.

## SMART GOAL WITH "SO THAT " STATEMENT

Ministry: _____ Date: _____

| List Goal statement below: |
| --- |
| |

WRITE ONE STATEMENT PER PAGE WITH ACTION PLANS BELOW

| WHAT ARE WE DOING? | WHO WILL DO IT? (NAME) | BY WHEN WILL WE COMPLETE THIS TASK? MM/DD/YY | RESOURCES NEEDED | ADDITIONAL COMMENTS |
| --- | --- | --- | --- | --- |
| | | | | |
| | | | | |
| | | | | |
| | | | | |
| | | | | |
| | | | | |
| | | | | |
| | | | | |
| | | | | |
| | | | | |
| | | | | |
| | | | | |
| | | | | |

USE ADDITIONAL PAGES AS NEEDED TO CLEARLY COMMUNICATE
YOUR TASK TO ACCOMPLISH THE GOAL

# Guiding Principle

**Provide clear steps along the pathway.**

Nothing is more frustrating than trying to meet expectations that are not clearly articulated.

So, how does the local congregation communicate the process of growing discipleship?

## Worship/Preaching

As presented in the "Passionate Worship" section of this Activation Guide, every worship service and particularly every worship message should provide clear next steps in becoming a growing disciple of Jesus.

Sometimes this is a practical step like "try this during your time at work this week." Sometimes it is an invitation to become involved in an educational opportunity or discipleship group that would be helpful in developing as a maturing disciple.

Worship is a primary entry point into the life of discipleship.

## Membership Expectations

As presented previously in this Guide, having clearly articulated expectations creates the culture of people living into those expectations. If there are not clearly articulated expectations, don't be surprised if people don't meet them!

This is one more reason a membership covenant is highly effective.

These expectations are explained as part of any new member class in the congregation.

## Informational Meetings

A good practice for growing congregations is to provide an opportunity for guests in worship to understand who you are as a church, what you stand for, and how you make a difference in people's lives.

This is a good place to cast a vision for intentional discipleship as practiced in your congregation.

## Brochures

Prepare a graphically designed brochure presenting your process. The following template may be helpful.

### WHERE ARE YOU?

| | Guest/Visitor | Regular Worship Attender | Beginning Believer | Growing Disciple | Maturing Disciple / Servant Leader |
|---|---|---|---|---|---|
| **Is this You?** | You have come to check out the church you are attending for the first time or sporadically. You may or may not have accepted Christ as your Savior. | You attend worship regularly or fairly often. You do not participate in the church beyond worship attendance. You may or may not have made a commitment to Christ. | You have recently committed or recommitted your life to Christ. You are a new Disciple and want to know more about how to live in this relationship. | You have been a Disciple for a while. You know the basics of the faith, have a daily time with God, engage in some form of accountable discipleship and serve others beyond the church. | You serve sacrificially. You are an influencer and leader in the faith community. You share your faith with those outside the church and disciple someone beginning the journey. You provide leadership in some ministry of the church. |
| **How to Grow to the Next Level** | Come back. Begin to worship regularly and participate in other ministries of the church. | Commit your life to Christ; engage in conversation with a nurturing disciple, form friendships with others in the church, and find a way to serve in a ministry of the church. | Learn about foundational spiritual practices, have a daily devotional time, explore Christian beliefs, connect with other disciples, give proportionately, and find a way to serve in the church. | Commit more of life to following God. Make your spiritual life a priority. Learn about spiritual practices, build relationships beyond the church to share Christ, tithe, and serve beyond the church. | Serve sacrificially in ministry. Continue to grow through spiritual practices, relationships with others, and service. Become a mentor or coach for newer disciples. Lead a ministry. |
| **Things You Can Do to Grow** | ☐ Learn about the church<br>☐ Meet people<br>☐ Ask questions about God<br>☐ Explore how the church engages the community | ☐ Connect with a faith guide<br>☐ Make a new friend at worship<br>☐ "Test-drive" a way of serving in the church<br>☐ Make a commitment to Jesus | ☐ Participate in a Foundations Class<br>☐ Participate in a Baptism Class<br>☐ Participate in a Walk to Emmaus<br>☐ Be baptized<br>☐ Begin a daily time with God<br>☐ Serve in a ministry<br>☐ Begin regular giving | ☐ Join a small discipleship group<br>☐ Attend a Companion in Christ Class<br>☐ Attend a SHAPE Class<br>☐ Attend a Financial Peace University Class<br>☐ Engage in daily spiritual practices<br>☐ Attend a Disciple Bible Study Class<br>☐ Tithe<br>☐ Explore a variety of ways to serve in ministry<br>☐ Get a Discipleship Coach | ☐ Continue to "feed yourself" through spiritual practices<br>☐ Become a spiritual mentor<br>☐ Become a Discipleship Coach<br>☐ Build relationships with non-believers to be Christ in their lives<br>☐ Provide leadership in an area of ministry<br>☐ Engage in personal missions<br>☐ Give generously (beyond a tithe) |

## Website

Cast a vision for discipleship as part of your website. Clearly articulate the process for your congregation.

## Congregational Interviews

Schedule an annual meeting with each of the members of your congregation. The primary focus should be "How is it with your soul?"

Practically, the question might be, "Since the church exists to help you grow as a disciple of Jesus, I am wondering how we might be more helpful."

How does your congregation articulate the discipleship process and encourage participation?

Build a SMART goal and action plan to advance your ideas for how you can promote discipleship through more effective communication.

## SMART GOAL WITH "SO THAT " STATEMENT

Ministry: _____ Date: _____

List Goal statement below:

WRITE ONE STATEMENT PER PAGE WITH ACTION PLANS BELOW

| WHAT ARE WE DOING? | WHO WILL DO IT? (NAME) | BY WHEN WILL WE COMPLETE THIS TASK? MM/DD/YY | RESOURCES NEEDED | ADDITIONAL COMMENTS |
|---|---|---|---|---|
| | | | | |
| | | | | |
| | | | | |
| | | | | |
| | | | | |
| | | | | |
| | | | | |
| | | | | |
| | | | | |
| | | | | |
| | | | | |
| | | | | |
| | | | | |
| | | | | |
| | | | | |

USE ADDITIONAL PAGES AS NEEDED TO CLEARLY COMMUNICATE
YOUR TASK TO ACCOMPLISH THE GOAL

## Shift 4

### From "Serve Us" to "Service

"Lord, when did we see you hungry or thirsty or a stranger or needing clothes or sick or in prison, and did not help you?" He will reply, "Truly I tell you, whatever you did not do for one of the least of these, you did not do for me."

—Jesus, Matthew 25:44–45

The world hears the Gospel when it sees it, when its witnesses are clearly committed to a more fully human future, in this world and the next.

—Albert Outler, Methodist Theologian

If your congregation suddenly disappeared, would the community mourn losing the blessings they provide?

—Rick Rusaw and Eric Swanson, The Externally Focused Church (1)

# Service Survey

The survey for this chapter will help you and your congregation explore the quality of your service opportunities. Service in the name of Jesus can be a vague and hard to define concept. These questions make specific connections to biblical guidelines for serving others in love.

## (1 = Poor . . . 4 = Amazing)

|  | Service | 1 | 2 | 3 | 4 |
|---|---|---|---|---|---|
| 1. | I have participated in a discipleship process for discovering my gifts and passions for ministry. |  |  |  |  |
| 2. | Someone from the congregation has had a discussion with me about how I might use my unique gifts and passions in ministry. |  |  |  |  |
| 3. | I am engaged in a ministry beyond the local church which makes a difference in someone's life. |  |  |  |  |
| 4. | This congregation offers a variety of opportunities for me to be engaged in ministry. |  |  |  |  |
| 5. | This congregation offers a variety of opportunities for me to exercise my faith through ministries of social justice. |  |  |  |  |
| 6. | I have built relationships with those whom this congregation is serving in the community. |  |  |  |  |
| 7. | I have participated on a mission team for either a local project or a short-term mission trip this year. |  |  |  |  |
| 8. | During worship, this congregation regularly celebrates lives that have been changed and the needs that have been met. |  |  |  |  |
| 9. | I am encouraged to pray for the needs of the community around me and for the world. |  |  |  |  |
| 10. | This congregation partners with other churches and social service agencies to provide a variety of services to meet the needs of this community. |  |  |  |  |

| | | | | | |
|---|---|---|---|---|---|
| 11. | My small group serves out in the community at least once a month. | | | | |
| 12. | There are regular testimonies during worship celebrating the difference this congregation is making in the community. | | | | |
| 13. | Our leadership team has done a demographic study to determine the needs of our local community. | | | | |
| 14. | Members of this congregation regularly interact with community leaders to determine how the church might best serve. | | | | |
| 15. | Our leaders model a life of service by personal engagement in ministries in the community. | | | | |
| 16. | This congregation receives offerings to support special needs in the community. | | | | |
| 17. | We track the service performed in the community to see if this congregation is growing in our 'heart' for others. | | | | |
| 18. | I serve in some way in the local community at least once a month. | | | | |
| 19. | This congregation has at least one ministry in the community that is a long-term relationship where the congregation is invited to engage and build relationships with those served. | | | | |
| 20. | Our leadership team has done in-depth analysis of community demographics to better understand the needs in the surrounding community. | | | | |
| 21. | Our church provides direct support for those in the community seeking meaningful employment. | | | | |
| 22. | Members of this congregation are encouraged to develop their personal ministries in response to identified community needs. | | | | |
| 23. | This congregation is known in the surrounding community for a ministry that is having significant impact. | | | | |
| 24. | I have participated in a short-term mission experience in another country or region of this country. | | | | |
| 25. | There are regular 'mission moments' in worship where the congregation learns about opportunities for service. | | | | |

A perfect score on this survey would be 100 points.

When using this with your leadership team or congregation, here is how you determine an average score: Total the points for each individual survey. Add the points from all the individual surveys together. Divide that total number by the number of surveys that were completed. This gives you an average score (out of 100 possible points), providing you with a "grade" for your congregational health in this area. Using a standard academic scale:

| | | |
|---|---|---|
| 90+ | = | A |
| 80-89 | = | B |
| 70-79 | = | C |
| 60-69 | = | D |

What grade does your service receive? What did the survey reveal? What is your strongest area? What do you want to hope for in service?

# Guiding Principle

**Jesus is already at work in the world. We are invited to join Jesus in ministry.**

*Shift 2.0* presents the framework of Micah 6:8 as a template for the service dimension of discipleship:

*Seek Justice . . . Love Mercy . . . Walk Humbly with Your God.*

**Mercy ministries** refer to the ways that we address the symptoms/needs of those outside the church. Churches are generally engaged in some way with mercy ministries:

- Food Pantries
- Meals for the homeless, hungry, lonely
- Thrift Stores
- Shelter (i.e. cold weather shelters)
- Medical Care.

**Justice ministries** address the causes that create the symptoms/needs:

- Tutoring/mentoring
- Job training/job creation
- Livable wages
- Affordable housing
- Burdensome ordinances
- Discipleship.

Walking humbly with our God addresses the spiritual lives of those coming to church. This is the foundation for effectiveness in both mercy and justice ministries and includes:

- Personal relationship with Jesus
- Spiritual practices
- Intentional relationships with those outside of the church
- Using gifts and graces to meet the needs of people outside the church.

## Defining Service

It is important to begin by coming to a common understanding of exactly what we mean by service (a category that for most local churches includes references to "outreach" and "missions").

# Team Activity!

**Defining Service:** Take a moment and list on a whiteboard or newsprint all the ways that people on your team perceive that your congregation is serving the community. Typical responses often include things like food pantry, meal for the homeless, Pumpkin Patch, VBS, Angel Tree at Christmas, Shoe Boxes at Christmas, Thanksgiving Meal for the Community, etc.

Write all the suggestions on the whiteboard or newsprint and then ask the question for each ministry identified: Do we actually connect with the persons we are seeking to serve in this instance? Do we have real conversations? Do we get to know them? Are we physically engaged with them?

Draw a line through all the items to which you responded "NO."

The remainder of the list may actually be service.

How did you do? What does this tell you about the level of service in your congregation?

To serve someone means that you engage them, face-to-face/ physically present, relationally connected.

Much of what churches call service is really generosity. It's a great thing for churches to be generous. But, let's not mistake it for service.

*Shift 2.0* presents what is called "The Graduate School of Ministry" (see below).

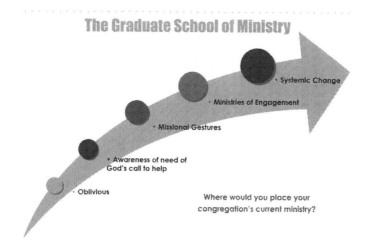

The Graduate School of Ministry

• Systemic Change

• Ministries of Engagement

• Missional Gestures

• Awareness of need of
God's call to help

• Oblivious

Where would you place your
congregation's current ministry?

As you review the list of items included on your service list (ways the church serves those outside), where does your church land on this spectrum?

• Missional gestures and ministries of engagement will be discussed later. For now, let's talk about them in terms of one-shot deals (missional gestures) and long term connections (ministries of engagement).

# Team Activity!

Impact Exercise: The following activity is designed to help your team dig a little deeper:

**In the columns below respond to the following:**

- **Who?** Make a list of people and groups in the community (outside of your members/regular worship participants) who are impacted by the ministry of your congregation.

- **What?** In the second column indicate the way(s) in which each are impacted. Be as specific as possible.

- **How Much?** In the last column rate the degree to which each of the people/groups would miss what it is that you do for thme if you were not providing this ministry. (1 = 'who?' and 10 = 'where do we turn now?')

| WHO? | WHAT? | HOW MUCH? |
|---|---|---|
|  |  |  |

A helpful point of conversation in reviewing the impact (how much?) is whether other organizations (non-profits, churches, community organizations) are providing a similar service and if it might be more helpful to direct energies another direction?

Build a SMART goal and action plan to advance your ideas for rethinking service projects in terms of becoming justice ministries and supporting justice ministries that already exist in your local community.

## SMART GOAL WITH "SO THAT " STATEMENT

Ministry: _____ Date: _____

| List Goal statement below: |
| --- |
| |
| |
| |

WRITE ONE STATEMENT PER PAGE WITH ACTION PLANS BELOW

| WHAT ARE WE DOING? | WHO WILL DO IT? (NAME) | BY WHEN WILL WE COMPLETE THIS TASK? MM/DD/YY | RESOURCES NEEDED | ADDITIONAL COMMENTS |
| --- | --- | --- | --- | --- |
| | | | | |
| | | | | |
| | | | | |
| | | | | |
| | | | | |
| | | | | |
| | | | | |
| | | | | |
| | | | | |
| | | | | |
| | | | | |
| | | | | |
| | | | | |
| | | | | |

USE ADDITIONAL PAGES AS NEEDED TO CLEARLY COMMUNICATE
YOUR TASK TO ACCOMPLISH THE GOAL

# Guiding Principle

**The church is at its best when we transform
lives, not just moments.**

## The mission of the church:

*Make disciples of Jesus Christ for the transformation of the world.*

The church got the order right on this. Transformation of the world begins with making disciples. If there are not growing, maturing disciples in our congregation, it will be difficult to sustain any kind of effort in transformation.

Phil suggests that there are two critical elements to making disciples of Jesus Christ who serve others in impactful ways:

- Clarity of expectations for church members/regular participants
- A clear pathway to discovering giftedness in service and deploying serving disciples to make a difference.

For example, *Shift 2.0* recommends a Membership Covenant like the following:

| Traditional Vows | Dimensions of Discipleship | Membership Covenant |
|---|---|---|
| Prayers | Opening to Jesus/ Obeying Jesus | Participate regularly in a small discipleship group or other accountable discipling relationship. |
| Presence | A Life of Worship | Participate in weekly worship at least 3 weekends each month unless prevented by illness or travel. |
| Gifts | A Life of Generosity | Commit to proportional giving to the ministries of this congregation and to moving toward a tithe. |
| Service | A Life of Service | Serve in some way in the local community (beyond the walls of the church) each month. |
| Witness | A Life of Hospitality | Invite someone to come with me to church/events at least three times per year and build at least three relationships outside the church to witness the love of Christ. |

How might this tool or some equivalent tool be helpful to your congregation in establishing expectations for service?

102

*Shift 2.0* also recommends a pathway for discovering how God has uniquely equipped each of us to serve, explores opportunities to try out various ways to serve, and engages each disciple in using their spiritual gifts and talents to make a difference. Consider the following progression from the previously referenced Real Discipleship Survey:

| A life of Service | I am amazed at the way some disciples selflessly serve others and I wnat to make a difference as well. | I know Christ invites me to join Him in serving others and I am discovering how God has gifted me to do this | I experiment serving in different areas as I discover my gifts, talents and passions | I join Jesus in mission to others using my God-given gifts, talents and passion |
|---|---|---|---|---|

To get a sense of where people in your congregation place themselves in the journey of A Life of Service as well as the other dimensions of a life of discipleship, go to emc3coaching.com and check out the Real Discipleship Survey.

## Approaches to Service Ministries

Previously, we explored briefly the distinction between missional gestures and ministries of engagement. Let's take a deeper look:

**Missional Gestures:** This is where we give support for something or someone to help those in need. A distinguishing factor for missional gestures is that they do not have people engaged in hands-on ministry and the related development of relationships with those being served. These are mostly one-time shots.

**Ministries of Engagement:** In a ministry of engagement the congregation not only provides resources for those with specific needs but also has direct contact with those being served. It is a long-term connection. This approach fosters the building of relationships so that those being served may come to know the love of Christ, and engages our hands and feet rather than just our pocketbooks. It also helps us grow in our understanding of the needs of those in our community so that we might address both mercy and justice issues.

# Team Activity!

**Missional Gestures vs. Ministries of Engagement**

Go back to the "Who, What, How Much" chart that you explored earlier. Which of these are missional gestures and which are ministries of engagement?

Which of these categories has the greatest potential for transforming the world?

What gifts, talents, and experiences does your congregation have to around a particular theme?

**Justice Ministries**

Let's be abundantly clear. Mercy ministries (providing for the needs of people outside the church) are really good things to be involved in. They give a 'helping hand' to those in need.

**But, mercy ministries do not transform the world.**

They might transform the moment in time – take away the hunger or provide a night's shelter from the cold. But they don't solve the problem.

Justice ministries work to address the core problem. It's the actualization of the old adage, "Give a man a fish and he won't be hungry. Teach a man to fish and he'll never be hungry again."

# Team Activity!

**Socially Transformative Ministries:** Scan the following "Social Creed of the United Methodist Church." Circle opportunities/themes that relate to justice ministries.

*We believe in God, Creator of the world; and in Jesus Christ, the Redeemer of creation. We believe in the Holy Spirit, through whom we acknowledge God's gifts, and we repent of our sin in misusing these gifts to idolatrous ends.*

*We affirm the natural world as God's handiwork and dedicate ourselves to its preservation, enhancement, and faithful use by humankind.*

*We joyfully receive for ourselves and others the blessings of community, sexuality, marriage, and the family.*

*We commit ourselves to the rights of men, women, children, youth, young adults, the aging, and people with disabilities; to improvement of the quality of life; and to the rights and dignity of all persons.*

*We believe in the right and duty of persons to work for the glory of God and the good of themselves and others and in the protection of their welfare in so doing; in the rights to property as a trust from God, collective bargaining, and responsible consumption; and in the elimination of economic and social distress.*

*We dedicate ourselves to peace throughout the world, to the rule of justice and law among nations, and to individual freedom for all people of the world.*

*We believe in the present and final triumph of God's Word in human affairs and gladly accept our commission to manifest the life of the gospel in the world. Amen.*

The chances are good that you identified themes like:

- Caring for creation
- Quality of life and dignity for all persons
- Meaningful work
- Responsible consumption.

There are a multitude of ways congregations can engage in any one of these themes for the transformation of the world.

*As a team, brainstorm about one theme to consider the possibilities for engaging in the transformation of the world. Try to identify at least 5 things a community of faith could do.*

*For example, a church Phil works with in Erie, PA has a ministry of building ramps on homes so that those with disabilities can have easier access. This certainly addresses the quality of life referenced in the Social Creed.*

1.

2.

3.

4.

5.

Build a SMART goal and action plan to advance your ideas
for transformative ministries of engagement in your community.

## SMART GOAL WITH "SO THAT " STATEMENT

Ministry: _____  Date: _____

List Goal statement below:

WRITE ONE STATEMENT PER PAGE WITH ACTION PLANS BELOW

| WHAT ARE WE DOING? | WHO WILL DO IT? (NAME) | BY WHEN WILL WE COMPLETE THIS TASK? MM/DD/YY | RESOURCES NEEDED | ADDITIONAL COMMENTS |
|---|---|---|---|---|
| | | | | |

USE ADDITIONAL PAGES AS NEEDED TO CLEARLY COMMUNICATE
YOUR TASK TO ACCOMPLISH THE GOAL

# Guiding Principle

**The church is most transformational when we
discern the needs of our community in partnership
with community residents and leaders, rather
than unilaterally proclaiming the needs of our
community and how we will address them.**

## Tools for Discernment

### MissionInsite Reports

In previous sections of the Activation Guide, your team has
had the opportunity to explore your community demographics
through MissionInsite. Up to this point you have been focused
on general demographics and Mosaic Group preferences (e.g.
worship style).

Another valuable report from MissionInsite is the Quad
Report that looks at values, beliefs, and even needs identified by
those in the study area.

With the Quad Report for your study area (church community) review the implications:

| | | Study Area | | US Average | |
|---|---|---|---|---|---|
| | | Modest Concern | Significant Concern | Modest Concern | Significant Concern |
| **Personal Life** | Average | 29.2% | 12.4% | 29.5% | 9.70% |
| Anger management/losing my temper | | 31.4% | 7.30% | 29.5% | 5.40% |
| Depression | | 35.5% | 13.4% | 35.9% | 10.4% |
| Finding a mate/spouse | | 17.4% | 11.0% | 15.2% | 7.40% |
| Getting over the past/dealing with guilt | | 37.1% | 11.0% | 37.7% | 7.80% |
| Losing weight/diet issues | | 44.0% | 26.5% | 48.4% | 22.4% |
| Making Friends | | 31.4% | 7.30% | 32.6% | 6.40% |
| Personal health problems | | 50.9% | 22.3% | 52.3% | 17.3% |
| Problems with addictions | | 11.5% | 5.30% | 11.9% | 3.50% |
| Struggling with my sexual orientation | | 4.50% | 2.90% | 3.60% | 1.70% |
| Unemployment/Losing my job | | 28.0% | 16.7% | 28.4% | 14.5% |
| **Home and Family** | Average | 24.3% | 10.1% | 24.2% | 7.80% |
| Avoiding homelessness | | 27.4% | 11.8% | 23.1% | 8.80% |
| Balancing work * family | | 31.7% | 10.6% | 33.1% | 8.50% |
| Caring for aging parnets | | 28.2% | 13.8% | 28.1% | 13.5% |
| Child who is gay, lesbian, bisexual or transgender | | 5.40% | 3.70% | 4.90% | 2.60% |
| Confilct resoultion/arguing too much | | 30.3% | 8.70% | 30.4% | 6.70% |
| Divorce | | 10.1% | 5.00% | 9.90% | 3.60% |
| Domestic violence in my family | | 9.80% | 3.60% | 7.10% | 2.40% |
| Health criss/illness | | 47.1% | 21.0% | 47.7% | 15.8% |
| Marriage problems | | 16.8% | 6.10% | 17.4% | 5.10% |
| Raising a teen | | 16.0% | 8.60% | 15.0% | 6.80% |
| Raising chidren as a single parent | | 9.30% | 7.80% | 7.90% | 4.40% |
| Stress/time to relax | | 44.9% | 21.2% | 48.6% | 16.3% |

*(This is a sample report. Please review the report from your study area.)*

## Acts 1:8 Exercise

This exercise (based of course on Acts 1:8) looks at the witness of the church (through the lens of ministry) to those in:

- Jerusalem (those that are already with you)
- Judea (those who are like you but not with you)
- Samaria (those who are different from you)
- Ends of the Earth (those far away from you).

# Team Activity!

In the columns below, identify characteristics of those in the Jerusalem and Judean groups. Note: avoid mushy things like friendly, compassionate, caring. Focus on identifiable characteristics like education level, ages, financial status, family make-up, entertainment, etc.

| Jerusalem Group | Judean Group |
|---|---|
|  |  |

Where are the gaps? What did you discover?

For example, a church in Delaware discovered that there were no (0%) single parent families involved in the life and ministry of the congregation. Yet, in the community surrounding the church, 23% of the homes were single parent households. This caused the church leadership to step back and ask why this apparent discrepancy exists.

What did you discover?

## Community Interviews

A critical tool for discerning the needs of the community is the Community Interview. The following framework is provided. A full-size, color version is available at emc3coaching.com by selecting the Resources Tab.

### Strategies for Getting to Know Your Community

• CONNECT WITH LOCAL BUSINESSES

• COMMUNITY INTERVIEWS

**Preparing for the Community Interviews**

Getting to know the community . . . personally!
While demographic studies are a very valuable tool,
nothing beats 'boots on the ground' when it comes to understanding the community you have been called to serve. Interviews with community leaders are an excellent way to uncover where the congregation can build bridges into the community.

Who might be helpful to interview? Think of persons who would be able to give you insights into community trends and needs. Such persons in your community might include:

• **Mayor**
• **Council Representatives**
• **Police Chief**
• **Fire Chief**
• **Home Owners'**
   **Association**
• **Realtors**
• **School Principals**
• **Hospital Administrators**
• **Social Service agencies**
• **Pastors of other**
   **congregations**
• **Chamber of Commerce**
• **Neighbors in your**
   **community**

**Who should make the interviews?** Involve people in the interviews who will represent the congregation well and who will be at ease speaking with community leaders. It also needs to be people who are able to ask leading questions and then listen and learn from what they hear.

**Keep the interviews simple:** The purpose of the interview is to listen. After greetings, give a simple explanation that your congregation is conducting a series of community leader interviews to discover ways in which they can be of greater service to others. Then ask the community leader the following open-ended questions and let them talk. The first question is designed to be an easy ice breaker:

• What do you like most about living in this community?
• What are the greatest needs that you see in our community?
• How might the church be of service to you and/or the community?
• Where do you already see people coming together to make good things happen?

**Preparing the Community Interviews Summary Report**
Since this is a summary report, keep it to no more than one or two pages. After listing who was interviewed and by whom, briefly share key discoveries around the following three questions:

• What are the greatest unmet needs in our community?
• Where might our congregation be a blessing to the community?
• Where is God already at work through others that the congregation might choose to support?

CONNECT!

©2016 EMC3 Coaching

111

## Prayer Walks

This is literally a "boots on the ground" exercise and a wonderful way to allow God to reveal to us the needs and possibilities for engaging our community. An Appendix at the end of this Activation Guide includes a description and guidance for leading Prayer Walks. A more complete discussion of Prayer Walks is included in the "'Serve Us' to Service" chapter in *Shift 2.0*.

# Team Activity!

**Needs Matrix Exercise:** The following table is designed to help your team identify the needs (left hand column) for a variety of demographic groups (top row). Take a few minutes with your team to identify some possibilities.

|  | The Poor | Children | The Aged | Widows/ Single Parents | Prisoners | The Sick/ Disabled | Immigrants |
|---|---|---|---|---|---|---|---|
| PHYSICAL |  |  |  |  |  |  |  |
| SPIRITUAL |  |  |  |  |  |  |  |
| SOCIAL |  |  |  |  |  |  |  |
| EMOTIONAL |  |  |  |  |  |  |  |
| EDUCATIONAL |  |  |  |  |  |  |  |
| VOCATIONAL |  |  |  |  |  |  |  |

For all needs addressed by other congregations or existing social service agencies place an X. The remaining are the gaps in service and opportunities for your congregation to make a significant difference.

## Engaging in Service

Levels of Engagement: Which of the following opportunities for ministry are provided and encouraged within your congregation?

| Opportunities | Notes: |
|---|---|
| Church Service: Opportunities for people to find a place to serve within the ministries of the church (essential for active assimilation) | |
| Missional On-ramps: Short-term, low commitment, non-threatening ways for people to explore types of service | |
| Community Service: Teams providing support for families in the community and/or supporting existing social service organizations | |
| Short-Term Missions: Teams providing support for hurricane recovery, flood recovery, tornado recovery etc., or working with the poor to provide shelter support | |
| Personal Ministry: The encouragement and challenge of members to find opportunities to engage in personal ministry to someone in the community. | |

# Inviting to Service Engagement

How does your congregation invite people to take next steps in service?

| Method | Notes: |
|---|---|
| Preaching about service | |
| Teaching about service | |
| Clear service dimension to discipleship | |
| Praying for the community – in worship and personal prayer | |
| Celebrating service – witnesses/testi-monies | |

Build a SMART goal and action plan to formulate ideas for discerning the true needs of your local community.

## SMART GOAL WITH "SO THAT " STATEMENT

Ministry: _____ Date: _____

List Goal statement below:

WRITE ONE STATEMENT PER PAGE WITH ACTION PLANS BELOW

| WHAT ARE WE DOING? | WHO WILL DO IT? (NAME) | BY WHEN WILL WE COMPLETE THIS TASK? MM/DD/YY | RESOURCES NEEDED | ADDITIONAL COMMENTS |
|---|---|---|---|---|
| | | | | |
| | | | | |
| | | | | |
| | | | | |
| | | | | |
| | | | | |
| | | | | |
| | | | | |
| | | | | |
| | | | | |
| | | | | |
| | | | | |
| | | | | |
| | | | | |
| | | | | |

USE ADDITIONAL PAGES AS NEEDED TO CLEARLY COMMUNICATE
YOUR TASK TO ACCOMPLISH THE GOAL

# Guiding Principle

**Disciples make the greatest impact and are most blessed when serving out of their spiritual gifts and graces.**

## A Biblical Model for Ministry

*Shift 2.0* makes a strong distinction between the consumer model where the pastor is basically considered to be hired to do ministry and the biblical model where the pastor is tasked with equipping the congregation for ministry. Take a moment to review the following considerations:

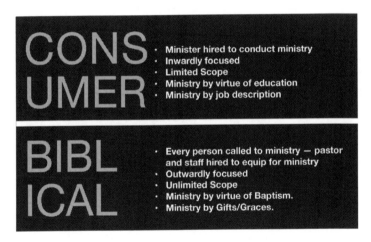

CONS UMER
- Minister hired to conduct ministry
- Inwardly focused
- Limited Scope
- Ministry by virtue of education
- Ministry by job description

BIBL ICAL
- Every person called to ministry — pastor and staff hired to equip for ministry
- Outwardly focused
- Unlimited Scope
- Ministry by virtue of Baptism.
- Ministry by Gifts/Graces.

## Personal Ministry Discernment

If the role of the church is to equip people for ministry, what are some considerations for making this happen? *Shift 2.0* suggests the following:

### Discipleship Process

One of the dimensions of discipleship presented in the "Membership to Discipleship" section of this guide was the Life of Service.

In considering a Life of Service, the first movement towards maturity is helping the disciple discern how God has equipped them for ministry. Often, the church seeks to accomplish this by offering a 'Spiritual Gifts Inventory'. We consider this just a first step in discernment. A more comprehensive approach is recommended, recognizing that God can use more than just our identified spiritual gifts. We have talents, passions, personalities, and life experiences that all impact the type of service that both blesses and is a blessing.

A variety of options are available to support this discernment, including:

# WIRED FOR MINISTRY

This process of discernment is recommended to be included as part of the intentional discipleship process.

What does your church offer to support this discernment?

## Training Options

Beyond the discernment process, it is recommended that disciples be trained to engage effectively with the persons they will be serving. This lack of understanding is often an obstacle to people having a level of comfort with engaging the community.

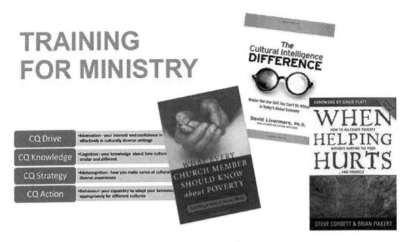

The following resources are suggested:

## On-ramp explorations

One of the keys for helping disciples discover their calling is to provide opportunities for them to try on various service opportunity to determine the 'fit'. There are several ways to accomplish this:

- Provide a listing of service opportunities for people to explore.
- Sponsor teams from the church to engage in entry level opportunities.
- Include a service dimension to all small groups in the church (suggested in "Membership to Discipleship").

## Celebration of Service

Just like congregations celebrate the work of mission teams (regional or international) and celebrate the financial commitment of members during stewardship campaigns, it is helpful to use worship services to recognize those providing service to the community:

- Mention them in a message.

118

- Provide testimonies about their impact.

- Create a written or video record of stories of impact for use in ministry publications and posting on social media.

- Provide personal recognition by taking them out to lunch or meeting for coffee.

How does your congregation equip, deploy, and celebrate those who serve? Build a SMART goal and action plan to generate ideas that answer these questions more fully.

## SMART GOAL WITH "SO THAT " STATEMENT

Ministry: _____   Date: _____

List Goal statement below:

WRITE ONE STATEMENT PER PAGE WITH ACTION PLANS BELOW

| WHAT ARE WE DOING? | WHO WILL DO IT? (NAME) | BY WHEN WILL WE COMPLETE THIS TASK? MM/DD/YY | RESOURCES NEEDED | ADDITIONAL COMMENTS |
|---|---|---|---|---|
| | | | | |
| | | | | |
| | | | | |
| | | | | |
| | | | | |
| | | | | |
| | | | | |
| | | | | |
| | | | | |
| | | | | |
| | | | | |
| | | | | |
| | | | | |
| | | | | |

USE ADDITIONAL PAGES AS NEEDED TO CLEARLY COMMUNICATE
YOUR TASK TO ACCOMPLISH THE GOAL

# Shift 5

## From "Survival Mentality" to "Generosity"

The generous will themselves be blessed,
for they share their food with the poor.

—Proverbs 22:9

In everything I did, I showed you that by this kind of hard work we
must help the weak, remembering the words the Lord Jesus himself
said: "It is more blessed to give than to receive."

—Acts 20:35

"Earn all you can, save all you can, give all you can."

—John Wesley, founder of Methodism

# Generosity Survey

A survey to be completed by leadership and congregation members to evaluate the quality of generosity within your church. After reading the statement to the left, rate your response from 1-4 with 4 representing strong agreement and 1 representing disagreement.

(1 = Poor . . . 4 = Amazing)

| | **Extravagant Generosity** | 1 | 2 | 3 | 4 |
|---|---|---|---|---|---|
| 1. | Our congregation celebrates the generosity of members through regular testimonies. | | | | |
| 2. | I give at least a tithe (10%) of my income to support the ministries of this congregation. | | | | |
| 3. | This congregation provides opportunities to grow in the understanding and ability to be a good steward. | | | | |
| 4. | This congregation looks for opportunities to support those in need in the community. | | | | |
| 5. | Our tithes and offerings are received joyously as an act of worship. | | | | |
| 6. | Our pastor regularly preaches about financial stewardship as a spiritual discipline. | | | | |
| 7. | Our congregation conducts an annual stewardship emphasis that encourages members to take the next step in generosity. | | | | |
| 8. | Clear expectations have been communicated to members and participants about financial commitments to the ministries of the church. | | | | |
| 9. | The pastor is aware of the giving patterns for each family in the congregation. | | | | |
| 10. | As the offering is received, someone shares how the resources provided are making a difference. | | | | |

| | | | | | |
|---|---|---|---|---|---|
| 11. | A criterion for positions of leadership is that the person is tithing toward the ministries. | | | | |
| 12. | A biblical financial management course is offered as part of the discipleship core curriculum. | | | | |
| 13. | The congregation is encouraged to live within financial margins in order to respond to needs encountered as a life-style of generosity. | | | | |
| 14. | Persons are encouraged to eliminate credit card debt before becoming tithers. | | | | |
| 15. | A commitment of proportional giving and moving toward tithing is an expectation of membership. | | | | |
| 16. | Leaders in this congregation model a lifestyle of generosity through tithing and sacrificial giving. | | | | |
| 17. | This congregation provides a tithe or more in support of ministry beyond the walls of the church. | | | | |
| 18. | There is a sense of transparency about the way resources are utilized in ministry. | | | | |
| 19. | This church provides a budget that clearly articulates the support of ministries that align with the vision and mission of the congregation. | | | | |
| 20. | This congregation focuses on the needs of the community before the needs of its members. | | | | |
| 21. | The resources of ministries for this congregation are primarily (90%) funded through the contributions of members. | | | | |
| 22. | The financial support for ministries of this congregation is growing each year. | | | | |
| 23. | There is a clear sense of mission and vision which drives the financial decisions of this congregation. | | | | |
| 24. | The ministries of this congregation are led by members rather than staff, limiting the staff costs to around 35% of the budget. | | | | |
| 25. | A contingency fund of 5-6% of the annual budget is in place. | | | | |

A perfect score on this survey would be 100 points.

When using this with your leadership team or congregation, here is how you determine an average score: Total the points for each individual survey. Add the points from all the individual surveys together. Divide that total number by the number of surveys that were completed. This gives you an average score (out of 100 possible points), providing you with a "grade" for your congregational health in this area. Using a standard academic scale:

| | | |
|---|---|---|
| 90+ | = | A |
| 80-89 | = | B |
| 70-79 | = | C |
| 60-69 | = | D |

What grade does your generosity receive? What did the survey reveal? What is your strongest area? What do you want to hope for in financial generosity?

# Guiding Principle

## Generosity is a spiritual issue.

In the church we often treat the money side of operations as the business dimension of our ministry with little or no thought given to the connection of finances to our spiritual lives. Yet, how we use our resources (financial as well as time and energy) is very much a spiritual issue. It reflects where we find our personal worth, our values, our security, and our joy in life.

That's why the Apostle Paul, in 1 Timothy, writes:

For the love of money is a root of all kinds of evil.
Some people eager for money, have wandered from the faith
and pieced themselves with many griefs.

**--1 Timothy 6:10 (NIV)**

124

Money is just "a" root of evil, not "the" root. But the pursuit of money can be a distraction and even a replacement for the relationship God wants with us.

That's why God calls us to use 100% of our resources in ways that honor God and why God established the tithe – an 'off-the-top' commitment of 10% of our income – to the ministry of the people of God. It recognizes that everything we have is a gift from God to be used to bring glory and honor to God. It reminds us that we are ultimately dependent on God. It provides us with a tangible way that we demonstrate that God has first place in our lives.

This Kingdom perspective is at 180 degrees from the perspective and practices of the culture around us. There is even a name given to the cultural perspective: Affluenza – the disease of affluence. Its hallmarks are:

- Materialism: Finding our worth, value, security, in the stuff we have rather than our relationship with God.

- Consumerism: The need for more and more stuff, believing this stuff will make us happy rather than the joy of our relationship with God.

- Easy Debt: The bondage of using resources we don't have to buy stuff we don't need, making us slaves to the creditor.

Research shows that a significant percentage of people carry credit card debt of over $10,000, have little or no savings, cannot cover an emergency of even $1,000, have little to nothing saved for retirement, and give about 2.9% to the church.

# Team Activity!

Demographic Study: To get an insight into how big an issue this is for your congregation, review the MissionInsite Quick-Insite Report and the Missional Vital Sign of Annual Giving for your congregation.

- What is the annual income level for your study area?

- What would a tithe of that income level be?

In reviewing the Annual Giving, take the total giving for the year and divide by the number of giving units or potential giving units for your congregation.

- What is the giving level per family/giving unit?

- How does this compare to the 'tithe' calculation for the average annual income level for your area?

- *There are, of course, many factors influencing the giving level in your congregation. For example, you may be engaging primarily a retired demographic living on a fixed income, or you may be reaching primarily the working poor. These are certainly factors for continued conversation.*

Often the approach in local congregations to dealing with Affluenza is to have a stewardship campaign where the focus is getting people to understand that the biblical standard for faithful stewardship is the 10% tithe. You may, however, find this approach to be counter-productive.

*Shift 2.0* suggests the Andy Stanley approach of helping people see what God wants for them financially rather than what the church wants from them. For example, God wants us to:

- Be thankful for all that God provides

- Be content with what God has provided

- Be faithful in using what God has provided

- Be available to respond when God puts a need in our life path.

A more helpful approach to dealing with Affluenza is to help people make these shifts in perspective. This is done as we help them discover the Life of Generosity pathway described in the "Membership to Discipleship" section of this Activation Guide. Generosity is a spiritual issue and should be part of an intentional discipleship process.

Phil suggests starting with establishing clear expectations and suggests a membership covenant:

| Traditional Vows | Dimensions of Discipleship | Membership Covenant |
|---|---|---|
| Prayers | Opening to Jesus/ Obeying Jesus | Participate regularly in a small discipleship group or other accountable discipling relationship. |
| Presence | A Life of Worship | Participate in weekly worship at least 3 weekends each month unless prevented by illness or travel. |
| Gifts | A Life of Generosity | Commit to proportional giving to the ministries of this congregation and to moving toward a tithe. |
| Service | A Life of Service | Serve in some way in the local community (beyond the walls of the church) each month. |
| Witness | A Life of Hospitality | Invite someone to come with me to church/events at least three times per year and build at least three relationships outside the church to witness the love of Christ. |

How does your congregation communicate expectations? How might framing expectations from the perspective of "what God wants for you" be helpful?

A Life of Generosity is something we need to be trained to live into. A surprising percentage of people do not have a personal budget or investments of any kind, and some don't even know how to balance their checkbook. Their lives are certainly not formed around the basic biblical understandings for the use of financial resources. This is not something the church should avoid. After all, Jesus talked a lot about money and its impact on our spiritual journey.

Phil recommends that training in biblical financial management be part of an intentional discipleship process and suggests a variety of resources that may be helpful, including:

## Discerning the call to Generosity

A more complete listing of suggested resources is found in *Shift 2.0*.

Notice the language of 'trained' instead of 'taught'. While there is certainly an educational component to helping people develop a Life of Generosity, just knowing about something doesn't always translate into practice. This is where Discipleship Coaches, Mentors, and even small groups can be helpful in bringing a level of accountability.

How does your church train people to live generously? What resources and relationships do you provide to accomplish this? How is this built into your discipleship process?


## Preaching and Teaching Stewardship

It is a good practice in local congregations to conduct an annual stewardship campaign. This usually involves several weeks of messages around faithful stewardship and an opportunity to make a next level commitment in annual giving.

A variety of very good resources are available to support annual stewardship campaigns. A list of suggestions is found in *Shift 2.0*.

Whether this campaign is done to actually build the church budget for the next year or just to encourage faith-promise giving, it is a helpful tool for keeping the congregation mindful of this dimension of their spiritual lives.

In many congregations, the topic of money is avoided except for this designated yearly campaign. *Shift 2.0* suggests that this is a mistake. Regular reference to generosity as part of our faithful discipleship should be part of our Sunday morning messages. Testimonies about the difference faithful steward-ship is making in people's lives is helpful year-round. Offering mission moments as the offering is introduced is a great way to help people 'connect the dots' about the ways that their giving is impacting lives and communities.

How does your congregation keep the theme of generosity as part of a discipleship journey at the forefront of congregational life?

## Legacy Giving

Phil notes in *Shift 2.0* that a relatively small percentage of congregations provide any direct support for legacy giving – including the ministries of the congregation in wills. While some people will naturally think about the church in their estate planning, for others it just may not come to mind. Why leave this to chance?

Most Judicatories (Annual Conferences for my Methodist friends) have a "foundation" in place through the Conference offices. These foundations not only provide funding for capital resources, they provide assistance for planning estates.

How has your congregation supported the development of estate planning? What resources are available?

## The Role of Leadership

The old quip that followers follow where leaders lead is certainly true when it comes to encouraging a Life of Generosity. If the leaders of the congregation are not modeling faithful stewardship, it is unlikely that the congregation will behave any differently.

Some congregations use a leadership application when considering people for elected leadership roles within the congregation. One of the questions often asked is, "Are you tithing?" (giving 10% of your income to the ministry of the church).

How does your congregation assure that leaders model the spiritual life sought for all members?

## Rethinking the Finance Committee

Most congregations have a group of people (committee, team, board) that are given responsibility for the management of finances. It puts together the annual budget which is then approved by a larger group (administrative council or congregation). Then in regular (often monthly) meetings, this group reviews the financial report (revenue and expenses) and monitors the way resources are being utilized. In lean financial times (e.g. summer) the committee asks staff and ministry teams to limit expenditures, and in stronger financial times it explores ways to invest in growth and prepare for contingencies.

Part of the responsibility of this committee is to prepare regular reports on the financial status of the congregation.

This role is often perceived as controlling and limiting ministries.

What is missing in many congregations is a group responsible for not just managing the available finances but creating the revenues available to accomplish ministry.

What if the role of Finance Committee were transitioned from managing finances to financial stewardship? What if this team were to take responsibility for supporting the Life of Generosity dimension of the discipleship process? What could happen if this team were to provide opportunities for legacy giving? Or submit grant applications for specific ministries? Or build donor relationships with those having the spiritual gift of generosity?

## The Ministry of the Ask

It is often the perspective of pastors and church leaders that it would be unseemly to directly ask someone with potential resources to make a generous gift to support a particular project or launch a new ministry.

This is a self-limiting perspective. There are people in most congregations with the potential resources to help the church make a big impact. But most of the time they will wait until someone asks them to help make a dream a reality.

It is actually a gift to them to be asked. They want to help. They want to make a difference. They just don't know how, and merely giving to the general fund doesn't seem to be helping the church reach its vision.

# Generosity as Pastoral Care

There is a lot of conversation in the church about whether a pastor should know the giving level of church members. Some churches have even instituted policies denying the pastor access to that information.

All churches should be aware that the 2016 General Conference passed legislation that reads,

> "[T]he pastor, in cooperation with the financial secretary, shall have access to and responsibility for professional stewardship of congregational giving records."
>
> **–Paragraph 340.c(2)(c)**

There are a couple of reasons this is important for the pastor to know:

- Giving is a spiritual issue and pastors are charged with the spiritual care of the congregation.

- From a pastoral care perspective, when the giving level dramatically changes, it may be an indication of a pastoral care need by that family.

- From a congregational conflict perspective, a change in giving by a family may be an indication that there is some type of conflict with the church. People tend to vote with their pocketbooks.

How does your congregation deal with pastoral access to financial giving records? Are you in line with the *Book of Discipline*?

Build a SMART goal and action plan for refining your approach to teaching stewardship.

## SMART GOAL WITH "SO THAT " STATEMENT

Ministry: _____ Date: _____

List Goal statement below:

WRITE ONE STATEMENT PER PAGE WITH ACTION PLANS BELOW

| WHAT ARE WE DOING? | WHO WILL DO IT? (NAME) | BY WHEN WILL WE COMPLETE THIS TASK? MM/DD/YY | RESOURCES NEEDED | ADDITIONAL COMMENTS |
|---|---|---|---|---|
| | | | | |
| | | | | |
| | | | | |
| | | | | |
| | | | | |
| | | | | |
| | | | | |
| | | | | |
| | | | | |
| | | | | |
| | | | | |
| | | | | |
| | | | | |
| | | | | |
| | | | | |

USE ADDITIONAL PAGES AS NEEDED TO CLEARLY COMMUNICATE
YOUR TASK TO ACCOMPLISH THE GOAL

# Guiding Principle

**To thrive, not just survive, give yourselves away.**

In a culture where church attendance is waning (as once-a-month becomes the new norm for 'regular attendance'), the duty of tithing is a thing of previous generations, people do not trust the church to use finances wisely, and where we are infected with the culture of Affluenza, it is often the response of the church to 'circle the wagons'.

This results in:

- Cutting ministry expenditures (especially beyond the walls of the church)
- Focusing the use of resources to take care of our own
- Doing whatever it takes to 'survive'.

The church is not called to survive. It is called to thrive.

The common responses to limited resources are exactly the things that are going to move the church into the realm of unsustainability. It reinforces the cultural perspective that all the church cares about is itself. This gives credence to the practice of not getting involved with a church or supporting a church.

The folks at Reimagine Generosity suggest a shift from spoon to ladle thinking:

> After all, a spoon is for feeding yourself, but a ladle is for serving others. The "spoon" vs. "ladle" thinking illustrates a mindset that is counter culture. When we give up our spoon and pick up a ladle, we are following the example of Christ by choosing to think of others needs ahead of our own. This kind of generosity does not come easily and always moves us beyond our comfort zone. For some, "ladle thinking" does mean writing a check; for others, it involves inviting someone into their life or taking the time to serve another person. "Ladle thinking" requires

faith and dependence on Christ. The "ladle" can manifest itself in different ways, but it always involves a putting off of selfish desires and a dependence on Christ.

One of the ways a church can get a handle on whether it is serving with a spoon (feeding ourselves) or with a ladle (thinking of others needs ahead of our own) is to calculate the percentage of the annual budget specifically set aside for making a difference in the community.

# Team Activity!

## Budgeting for the Community

- Take the total budgeted amount by the church for the year.
- Locate the line item(s) directly focused on supporting needs in the community (do not include any connectional giving expectations). Get a total.
- Calculate the percentage of the annual budget represented as supporting needs in the community.

For many churches this is a very small percentage. Phil describes working with a church where 0.03% of the budget was actually designated for community support. That means that the vast majority of resources were used to provide for the needs and wants of the congregation.

No wonder the culture perceives that we only care about ourselves.

How did your church measure up? What could be done to move this in a positive direction?

*Shift 2.0* suggests that local congregations should aim for a tithe of their resources to support needs in the community. What would it take for your church to get there?

## Five Giving Pockets

The reality is that most people don't give because of a duty but because they care about something, have a passion for something, or are inspired by something.

*Shift 2.0* presents 5 giving pockets or motivations for giving:

- The Bill Pocket: Giving to the general fund to help the church pay its bills.
- The Missions Pocket: Giving to support local mission and outreach and the work of missionaries sponsored by the church.
- The Education Pocket: Giving support to educational support in the local church as well as institutions of higher learning.
- The Benevolence Pocket: Giving to the poor and needy, supporting the ministries sponsored by the church.
- The Building Pocket: Giving for the brick and mortar facilities.

If these are the five motivations for giving, the question for the local church becomes how the opportunities for giving might be framed to encourage generosity.

# Team Activity!

**Pocket Exercise:** Using the chart below, see if your team can identify at least 3 ways for each of the giving pockets to encourage generosity:

| | | |
|---|---|---|
| Bill Pocket | 1 | |
| | 2 | |
| | 3 | |
| | 4 | |
| | 5 | |

| | |
|---|---|
| **Missions Pocket** | 1 <br><br> 2 <br><br> 3 <br><br> 4 <br><br> 5 |
| **Education Pocket** | 1 <br><br> 2 <br><br> 3 <br><br> 4 <br><br> 5 |
| **Benevolence Pocket** | 1 <br><br> 2 <br><br> 3 <br><br> 4 <br><br> 5 |
| **Building Pocket** | 1 <br><br> 2 <br><br> 3 <br><br> 4 <br><br> 5 |

*Shift 2.0* references the book Servolution by Dino Rizzo. This is the story of The Healing Place Church in Baton Rouge, Louisiana that began as a failing church plant. Dino, the pastor, learned some significant lessons early in the ministry, but the one that stands out is:

- Being ridiculously generous is one of the most contagious things that can run through a church. We don't want to be known for our average generosity; we want to be a church that gives with extreme generosity.

- Ridiculous generosity is exactly what we received from God...the perfect example of extreme giving.

As a point of information, this church grew to 7,000 members in several locations, co-founded the Association of Related Churches, planted 63 churches, and founded Go Global Missions.

In only one place in Scripture God say "test me." It is to test God's generosity. In Malachi 3:10 we read:

Bring the whole tithe into the storehouse, that there may be food in my house. Test me in this," says the Lord Almighty, "and see if I will not throw open the floodgates of heaven and pour out so much blessing that there will not be room enough to store it.

**–Malachi 3:10, NIV**

Most of the time this is preached as a personal discipleship text. But we wonder what could happen if churches were to trust God.

Build a SMART goal and action plan to generate ideas that
reflect a priority to budget with the community in mind.

## SMART GOAL WITH "SO THAT " STATEMENT

Ministry: _____ Date: _____

| List Goal statement below: |
| --- |
| |
| |
| |
| |

WRITE ONE STATEMENT PER PAGE WITH ACTION PLANS BELOW

| WHAT ARE WE DOING? | WHO WILL DO IT? (NAME) | BY WHEN WILL WE COMPLETE THIS TASK? MM/DD/YY | RESOURCES NEEDED | ADDITIONAL COMMENTS |
| --- | --- | --- | --- | --- |
| | | | | |
| | | | | |
| | | | | |
| | | | | |
| | | | | |
| | | | | |
| | | | | |
| | | | | |
| | | | | |
| | | | | |
| | | | | |
| | | | | |
| | | | | |
| | | | | |
| | | | | |

USE ADDITIONAL PAGES AS NEEDED TO CLEARLY COMMUNICATE
YOUR TASK TO ACCOMPLISH THE GOAL

# Guiding Principle

**People support organizations they trust to make an impact.**

According to *The Nonprofit Almanac,* 67% of Americans
engage in charitable giving.  Of those giving to charities,
56% will give to secular organizations and 45% will give to
religious organizations.  The average giving for religious
organizations is 1.8%.

> --National Center for Charitable Statistics

A couple of observations:

- The average giving to religious organizations falls well
  below a tithe.
- A greater percentage of people give to secular organizations
  than religious.

There seems to be a reason for this: **Trust.**

From the perspective of non-church-related institutions,
donors are most comfortable giving to institutions which are
clear and transparent about where every penny is spent, and
they are most inspired about giving to institutions in which
their generosity makes a discernible difference.

Churches are notorious for giving very little information
about the finances of the church.  Perhaps it is part of our
general reluctance to talk about money, but it could be bigger
than that.  It could be that we don't want people to really be
aware of how little of the resources provided actually go to
impacting the community.

So, we give tidbits that provide little to no information:

| | |
|---|---|
| This week's giving: | $XXX.xx |
| Year to Date giving: | $XXXX.xx |

Budgeted:      $XXXXXX.xx

Balance:       ($XXXX)

It's time to change this. Churches that do generosity well are transparent and inspirational. We'll discuss the inspirational part in the next section. For now, suffice it to say that people give (whether to a secular charity or to a church) when they know that their generosity is making a discernible difference.

So, how do we provide the transparency mentioned above?

The primary tool is the annual budget. (By the way, a surprising number of churches – like people – do not have a formal budget.)

The most common approach is the line item budget:

## First Church 2019 Budget

| AREA | BUDGETED | ACTUAL | VARIANCE |
|---|---|---|---|
| Ministry Expenses | | | |
| Children's Ministry | $34,000 | $26,500 | $(7,500) |
| Youth Ministry | 40,000 | 33,000 | (7,000) |
| Traditional Service | 3,500 | 3,000 | (500) |
| Contemporary Service | 3,500 | 3,650 | 150 |
| Fellowship | 12,000 | 5,500 | (6,500) |
| | | | |
| Trustees & Building | | | |
| | | | |
| Utilities | $22,000 | $18,350 | $(3,650) |
| Building Upkeep | 18,000 | 17,000 | (1,000) |
| Parking Lot | 600 | 120 | (480) |
| Telephones | 1,300 | 2,230 | 930 |
| | | | |
| Missions | $22,300 | $19,000 | (3,300) |
| | | | |

It is full of detail but does little to communicate how resources are utilized in a format that the average person in worship can understand. It's a great tool for your financial people.

A stronger approach for communicating how resources are utilized is the Program Budget.

## Program Budget Expenses
## $400,000

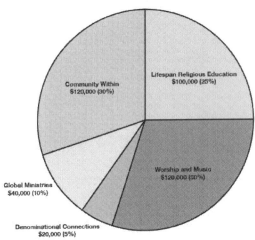

The Narrative Budget is an even stronger tool, helping people see how their resources are making an impact.

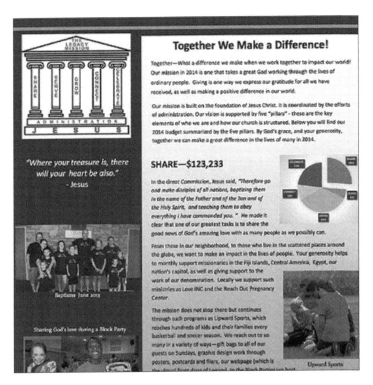

In a visually-oriented culture, seeking transparency and clear impact this is a strong choice.

How does your congregation communicate financial commitments and demonstrated impact?

- Is the budget built around the needs and vision of the congregation?
- Is the vision communicated clearly?
- Are regular financial reports available?
- Is the congregation aware of financial challenges?
- Are there policies to avoid debt and avoid spending all the resources on the congregation?

*Shift 2.0* suggest the following guidelines for building the church budget. How does your congregation match up with these?

| | |
|---|---|
| 33/33/33% basic distribution for staff/ programs/facilities- after community tithe | |
| Staff; 33-50% of total budget | |
| Contingency Fund of 5-6% | |
| Tithing to meet needs in the community | |
| Connectional Giving | |

The following sources of income are identified with some thoughts about their impact. How do these speak to your situation?

| | |
|---|---|
| Financial support by the congregation | This should be the primary source of income with projected budget around 80% of stewardship commitments.<br><br>As a general rule you can expect about $1000/person in average worship attendance each year. |
| Rental of Facilities | It is recommended that 20% or less of your budget be based on rental income – undependable, not biblical, and makes you the landlord rather than giver to community. |
| Fundraisers | As a general rule of thumb, fundraisers are best used to support special ministries (e.g. mission trips) rather than a revenue source for the budget. |
| Endowments | Many congregations use the interest to support general budget needs. |
| Designated Funds | Must be used as designated by the giver. |

Build a SMART goal and action plan to build a stronger connection between congregational giving and community impact.

## SMART GOAL WITH "SO THAT " STATEMENT

Ministry: _____ Date: _____

List Goal statement below:

WRITE ONE STATEMENT PER PAGE WITH ACTION PLANS BELOW

| WHAT ARE WE DOING? | WHO WILL DO IT? (NAME) | BY WHEN WILL WE COMPLETE THIS TASK? MM/DD/YY | RESOURCES NEEDED | ADDITIONAL COMMENTS |
|---|---|---|---|---|
| | | | | |
| | | | | |
| | | | | |
| | | | | |
| | | | | |
| | | | | |
| | | | | |
| | | | | |
| | | | | |
| | | | | |
| | | | | |
| | | | | |
| | | | | |
| | | | | |

USE ADDITIONAL PAGES AS NEEDED TO CLEARLY COMMUNICATE
YOUR TASK TO ACCOMPLISH THE GOAL

# Guiding Principle

**People today give because they are inspired, not out of duty.**

Consider the following giving patterns of various generations:

| Matures (born before 1945) | 60% donate to spiritual causes | Support: emergency relief, troops/veterans, the arts, political campaigns |
|---|---|---|
| Boomers (born between 1946 and 1964) | 48% donate to spiritual causes, want to know about finances before donating | Support: first responders |
| Generation X (born between 1965 and 1976) | 38% donate to spiritual causes | Support: health services, animal rights, environment |
| Millenials (born between 1977 and 1995) | 32% donate to spiritual causes | Support: human rights, child development, victims of crime and abuse |

# Team Activity!

**Generational Giving:** As you consider the demographic makeup of your congregation, what percentage fits into each of these generational categories?

What do you notice about the giving to spiritual causes? How might this impact your congregational giving in the future?

# Casting a Vision for Generosity

Consider the following suggestions for sharing your story and inviting people to support the work of the congregation:

- Tell stories from the perspective of someone who has been directly impacted by your ministry. Explain explicity how the generosity of your faith community made those moments possible.

- Have a staff member share inspirational stories about the work they are privileged to do and how generosity makes that work possible.

- Have someone who volunteered share inspiring stories about how they have seen God at work (in themselves and in others) through the work they have done with your ministry teams. Make the connection between that work happening and how generosity lays the foundation for it.

- Share an account of the difference being made by connectional giving. Be specific about what was accomplished and how a portion of every dollar given goes to make possible something that the local church could never do on its own without pooling its resources with other congregations.

For any of these personal witnesses it is easy to do a short video clip with a smartphone. This saves the intimidation factor of speaking in front of a group and allows you to control the time spent on the witness.

In the worship section of the Activation Guide, it was suggested that ministry moments be offered just prior to the offering time, highlighting some dimension of the ministry of the congregation. Even if not explicitly connected, the congregation will see how their generosity is making that possible.

Another way to highlight and celebrate the generosity of the congregation is to use time during pastoral messages to include illustrations about the impact being made through congregational generosity and faithfulness. This also supports the year-round stewardship emphasis.

A great resource for video witnesses to the impact church is making can be found at UMC.org.

Build a SMART goal and action plan to implement ideas to inspire people to give.

## SMART GOAL WITH "SO THAT " STATEMENT

Ministry: _____ Date: _____

List Goal statement below:

WRITE ONE STATEMENT PER PAGE WITH ACTION PLANS BELOW

| WHAT ARE WE DOING? | WHO WILL DO IT? (NAME) | BY WHEN WILL WE COMPLETE THIS TASK? MM/DD/YY | RESOURCES NEEDED | ADDITIONAL COMMENTS |
|---|---|---|---|---|
| | | | | |
| | | | | |
| | | | | |
| | | | | |
| | | | | |
| | | | | |
| | | | | |
| | | | | |
| | | | | |
| | | | | |
| | | | | |
| | | | | |
| | | | | |
| | | | | |

USE ADDITIONAL PAGES AS NEEDED TO CLEARLY COMMUNICATE YOUR TASK TO ACCOMPLISH THE GOAL

# Guiding Principle

**People don't give for the recognition,
but if they are not recognized they may stop giving.**

Don't miss this!

Be sure to thank people for their generosity. There are several forms of recognition:

- Personal recognition: Take the person to lunch or coffee to hear their story and share the difference they have made.

- Public celebration: If appropriate, mention the generosity (possibly in a ministry moment).

- Witnessing: Have a recipient of generosity share the impact on their lives in a ministry moment.

- Host an annual dinner (pull out all the stops for this one) to celebrate those who have made generous contributions to the ministry of the congregation. Honor each one, celebrating their impact.

- Use creativity to morph ideas into tangible experiences.

   ○ *Make a Blessings Tree.* Put a big Blessings Tree in your worship space and have people add 'leaves' on which they write the blessings in their lives and ministry.

   ○ *Life Inventory.* Give people a tool to sit down with their families and explore how they are setting their priorities and what their goals are for the future. Writing things down and discussing them can lead to revelations and realizations.

   ○ *Send handwritten notes.* Along with the 'stewardship package' that you send out to folks with your yearly budget appeal and prayer card, write a handwritten note thanking them for their generosity and what it means to your ministry. This is something you can even do at random times during the year! Youth can write notes giving thanks for support of the youth ministry! Children can write crayon-crafted notes giving thanks for support of the children's ministry!

∘ *Make special efforts to engage special supporters.* There is understandable resistance to this idea because we do not wish to show favoritism—the church has some unsavory history in this regard—but what we are talking about here is building relationships with people who have been blessed with resources that can help make vision happen. We are less queasy about focusing on these kinds of relationships with people with specific talents—we'll spend hours working with a creative team, musicians, or teachers. It is worthwhile to cultivate working relationships with those who have been blessed with financial resources, helping them understand more fully how God can make use of those blessings.

∘ Celebrate, celebrate, celebrate. Think of every way you can to celebrate service and generosity. Have a party. Have thanks-carolers call people up to sing them a 'thank you' song. Send a 'thank you' gift, a little ministry memento. Put up a wall of thanksgiving. Publicly recognize those who give—you don't do this by amounts, but say, for instance, you recognize those who have been giving continuously for the past 10 years. Lots of possibilities. Google "how to thank donors" and see which ideas can be adapted from the secular world to the ministry world.


How does your congregation cast the vision and celebrate the response for generosity? Build a SMART goal and action plan to create new ways to celebrate congregational giving.

## SMART GOAL WITH "SO THAT " STATEMENT

Ministry: _____ Date: _____

| List Goal statement below: |
| --- |
| |
| |
| |
| |

WRITE ONE STATEMENT PER PAGE WITH ACTION PLANS BELOW

| WHAT ARE WE DOING? | WHO WILL DO IT? (NAME) | BY WHEN WILL WE COMPLETE THIS TASK? MM/DD/YY | RESOURCES NEEDED | ADDITIONAL COMMENTS |
| --- | --- | --- | --- | --- |
| | | | | |
| | | | | |
| | | | | |
| | | | | |
| | | | | |
| | | | | |
| | | | | |
| | | | | |
| | | | | |
| | | | | |
| | | | | |
| | | | | |
| | | | | |

USE ADDITIONAL PAGES AS NEEDED TO CLEARLY COMMUNICATE
YOUR TASK TO ACCOMPLISH THE GOAL

# Appendix

## How to Conduct a Prayer Walk

### Prayer Walking with Your Community
### By Cheri R. Holdridge

**An Introduction: WHY DO WE WALK AND PRAY?**

Prayer is a precious gift. When we pray, we trust that God wants to communicate with us. When we pray, we open our side of communication with God. Because, you see, as every college freshman learns in Introduction to Speech class, communication takes two individuals, a speaker and a listener. In prayer, God always stands ready to listen. When we pray, we usually speak and we expect God to listen. In my own experiences of prayer, I find that prayer is deeper when I listen and wait for God to speak.

When we decide to "Prayer Walk" as individuals, or as communities of faith, we are seeking to connect in a deeper way with the communities in which we live and we are inviting God to speak to us. We are asking God to show us what we have failed to see. We are asking God to give us new eyes to see what has become invisible to us over time, and new ears to hear what has become "white noise" to us.

The act of walking gives out bodies something to do. The walking is a sort of calming distraction so that our minds and our souls can focus on listening to God.

Prayer walking has been one of the most amazing adventures of my life as a pastor and as a Jesus follower. I offer this prayer guide to you as an invitation. I hope it will help you listen for God, and see God more intimately in your communities.

### PRAYER WALK

You probably have picked up this guide because you and some of your friends or fellow church members want to connect in a deeper way to your neighborhood or community. The practice of Prayer Walking is just that: a practice. There really are no rules. What I can offer you are the suggestions of a seasoned pastor who has done her share of walking and praying and trying to discern God's call.

152

The first two tasks are to gather a group of people who want to go on a Prayer Walk and decide where you will take your Prayer Walk. If you are part of an existing church, and you want to connect in a fresh way with your neighbors, I suggest you lay out a plan to walk in a few blocks of your church building. If you are investigating an area for a church plant or a site for expansion ministry, then pick a location for your Prayer Walk where you want to explore opportunities for ministry. Again, lay out a plan to walk a few blocks in this neighborhood. If there is a school, neighborhood center, or other community gathering place nearby, include that place in your walk. If there are both residential and commercial streets near your church or mission area, try to include some of both in your Prayer Walks.

Hopefully you will have more than one Prayer Walk Team. A team will consist of two or three people. Have each team walk a different route, or if you walk the same routes, stagger your start times so that you are not clumped together. We do not want to overwhelm our neighbors with too many strangers gawking at them. Someone (a pastor, leader of your study process, or other person) should plan in advance what the routes will be, and prepare a simple map for each Prayer Walk Team. In planning the routes, remember that many of your folks may have been driving to your church for years but perhaps never have walked even one block in the neighborhood. (This fact in itself is telling.) So a map is essential. If you are in an inner city neighborhood, you may need to think about teaming people who are more comfortable in the city with people who are less comfortable walking in the city. Of course, walking in the daytime is probably better for everyone's comfort level in an unfamiliar place.

When you have gather your Prayer Walk Team of two or three people, sit down together and read through these questions. It will be better if you can put this paper aside during your walk, and just take in the experience. It is fine if you need to jot down a few key notes to help you remember, but try not to walk around the neighborhood with a clipboard, like you are taking a survey. Relax, and be ready to open your eyes and ears, to pray and soak up the experience with all of your senses.

For this first Prayer Walk we simply want to see our neighborhood with fresh eyes. We are on an expedition, a journey to learn as much as we can about the environment surrounding our church facility as we open our eyes and our hearts to our neighbors. We want to observe everything we can about our community, so we can being to get to know these strangers whose 'hood we visit every Sunday. Here are some things to look for:

1. What do the homes look like? What do you see in the yards and in the driveways? On the porches? Do they have driveways and porches? Is there landscaping? If so, what kind and how is it cared for?

2. What do the cars look like? Are they old or new? What makes and models are they? What kinds of bumper stickers do you see?

3. What people do you see and what evidence do you see of people? Are there children in this neighborhood? Bikes and toys? Are there senior citizens? People who like to garden or work on their cards? What race and possible nationality might the people be? Do you see any flags flying that give you signs of any ethnic heritage or any geographic background such as being from some particular part of the U.S. or from other countries?

# WHERE ARE YOU?

| | Guest/Visitor | Regular Worship Attender | Beginning Believer | Growing Disciple | Maturing Disciple / Servant Leader |
|---|---|---|---|---|---|
| **Is this You?** | You have come to check out the church you are attending for the first time or sporadically. You may or may not have accepted Christ as your Savior. | You attend worship regularly or fairly often. You do not participate in the church beyond worship attendance. You may or may not have made a commitment to Christ. | You have recently committed or recommitted your life to Christ. You are a new Disciple and want to know more about how to live in this relationship. | You have been a Disciple for a while. You know the basics of the faith, have a daily time with God, engage in some form of accountable discipleship and serve others beyond the church. | You serve sacrificially. You are an influencer and leader in the faith community. You share your faith with those outside the church and disciple someone beginning the journey. You provide leadership in some ministry of the church |
| **How to Grow to the Next Level** | Come back. Begin to worship regularly and participate in other ministries of the church. | Connect your life to Christ, engage in conversation with a maturing disciple, form friendships with others in the church, and find a way to serve in a ministry of the church. | Learn about foundational spiritual practices, have a daily devotional time, explore Christian beliefs, connect with other disciples, give proportionately, and find a way to serve in the church. | Commit more of life to following God. Make your spiritual life a priority. Learn about spiritual practices, build relationships beyond the church to share Christ, tithe, and serve beyond the church | Serve sacrificially in ministry. Continue to grow through spiritual practices, relationships with others and service. Become a mentor or coach for newer disciples. Lead a ministry. |
| **Things You Can Do to Grow** *(select options that meet your needs)* | ☐ Learn about the church<br>☐ Meet people<br>☐ Ask questions about God<br>☐ Explore how this church engages the community | ☐ Connect with a faith guide<br>☐ Make a new friend at worship<br>☐ Test-drive a way of serving in the church<br>☐ Make a commitment to Jesus | ☐ Participate in a Foundations Class<br>☐ Participate in a Beginnings Class<br>☐ Participate in a Walk to Emmaus<br>☐ Be baptized<br>☐ Begin a daily time with God<br>☐ Serve in a ministry<br>☐ Begin regular giving | ☐ Join a small discipleship group<br>☐ Attend a Companion in Christ Class<br>☐ Attend a SHAPE Class<br>☐ Attend a Financial Peace University Class<br>☐ Engage in daily spiritual practices<br>☐ Attend a Disciple Bible Study Class<br>☐ Tithe<br>☐ Explore a variety of ways to serve in ministry<br>☐ Get a Discipleship Coach | ☐ Continue to feed yourself through spiritual practices<br>☐ Become a spiritual mentor<br>☐ Become a Discipleship Coach<br>☐ Build relationships with non-believers to be Christ in their lives<br>☐ Provide leadership in an area of ministry<br>☐ Engage in personal missions<br>☐ Give generously (beyond a tithe) |

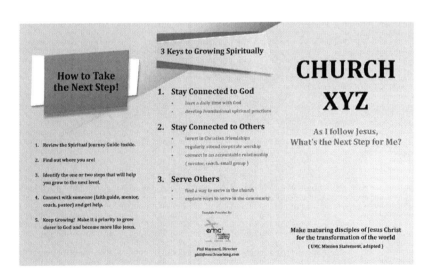

### How to Take the Next Step!

1. Review the Spiritual Journey Guide inside.

2. Find out where you are!

3. Identify the one or two steps that will help you grow to the next level.

4. Connect with someone (faith guide, mentor, coach, pastor) and get help.

5. Keep Growing! Make it a priority to grow closer to God and become more like Jesus.

### 3 Keys to Growing Spiritually

1. **Stay Connected to God**
   - have a daily time with God
   - develop foundational spiritual practices

2. **Stay Connected to Others**
   - invest in Christian friendships
   - regularly attend corporate worship
   - connect in an accountable relationship (mentor, coach, small group)

3. **Serve Others**
   - find a way to serve in the church
   - explore ways to serve in the community

Template Provided By:

Phil Maynard, Director
phil@emc3coaching.com

# CHURCH XYZ

As I follow Jesus,
What's the Next Step for Me?

Make maturing disciples of Jesus Christ for the transformation of the world
( UMC Mission Statement, adapted )

# Works Cited

## Shift 1

Michael Slaughter, Momentum for Life, Abingdon Press, Nashville, TN, 2005.

Bishop Robert Schnase, Five Practices of Fruitful Congregations, Abingdon Press, Nashville, TN, 2007.

MissionInsite, www.missioninsite .org.

Lovett Weems, Leadership in the Wesleyan Spirit, Abingdon Press, Nashville, TN, 1999.

## Shift 2

Louie Giglio, Wired For a Life of Worship: Student Edition of The Air I Breathe, Multnomah Books, Colorado Springs, CO, 2006.

## Shift 4

Rick Rusaw and Eric Swanson, The Externally Focused Church, Group Publishing, 2004.

*"Finally, there is a resource that invites individuals and small groups into a process of discovering a maturing relationship as disciples of Jesus Christ!"*

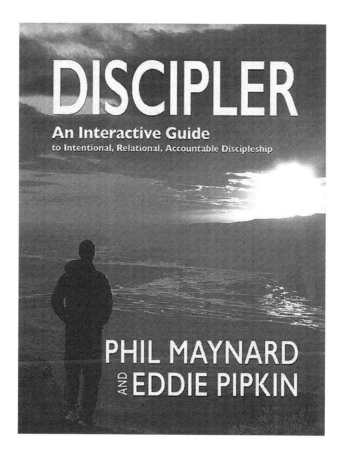

*Other new titles at MarketSquareBooks.com:*

Made in the USA
Columbia, SC
10 July 2019